Picture Maze
MARATHON

Picture Maze
MARATHON

Conceptis
Puzzles

STERLING INNOVATION
An imprint of Sterling Publishing Co., Inc.

387 Park Avenue South
New York, NY 10016
www.sterlingpublishing.com

STERLING, the distinctive Sterling logo, STERLING INNOVATION, and the Sterling Innovation logo are registered trademarks of Sterling Publishing Co., Inc.

2   4   6   8   10   9   7   5   3   1

Published by Sterling Publishing Co., Inc.
387 Park Avenue South, New York, NY 10016
© 2009 by Sterling Publishing Co., Inc.

Puzzles in this book previously appeared in *Picture This! Mazes*,
Hidden Picture Mazes, *Secret Picture Mazes*, and *Sneaky Picture Mazes*
Copyright © 2005 to 2007 by Conceptis Puzzles

Distributed in Canada by Sterling Publishing
c/o Canadian Manda Group, 165 Dufferin Street
Toronto, Ontario, Canada M6K 3H6
Distributed in the United Kingdom by GMC Distribution Services
Castle Place, 166 High Street, Lewes, East Sussex, England BN7 1XU
Distributed in Australia by Capricorn Link (Australia) Pty. Ltd.
P.O. Box 704, Windsor, NSW 2756, Australia

Manufactured in the United States of America
All rights reserved

Sterling ISBN 978-1-4027-6451-6

For information about custom editions, special sales, premium and
corporate purchases, please contact Sterling Special Sales
Department at 800-805-5489 or specialsales@sterlingpublishing.com.

CONTENTS

Introduction

Solve a maze and create a picture! There are two types of picture maze puzzles in this book, basic and reversed. To start out, solve each of these fun puzzles just as you would a traditional maze: find the true path by starting at the maze's entrance and drawing a line to the maze's exit, avoiding incorrect paths and dead ends.

But the fun is not over once you exit! What's next? In the basic kind of maze, you color in the path you traced with a dark, thick line of pen or marker to create a picture. In the other kind, which we call the reversed maze (labeled R), after you have traced the true path lightly in pencil, color in all the incorrect paths with a think pen or pencil to create your picture.

You might be surprised to learn that picture mazes of this kind were invented in Japan over 20 years ago. Today picture mazes have a dedicated following among children and adults all over the world. By reversing the tones of the maze paths, we can create more detailed pictures than are possible with basic picture mazes alone, as well as recognizable portrait mazes. So grab your marker and pencil and get started!

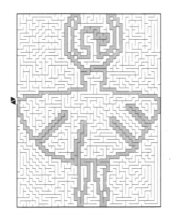

Solution on page 302

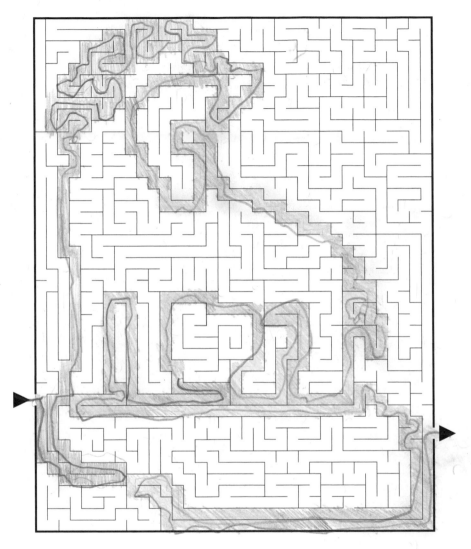

Solution on page 302

Maze #3

Solution on page 302

Maze #4

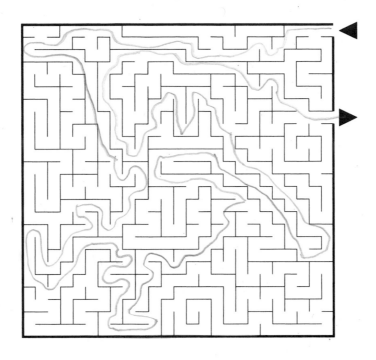

Maze #5

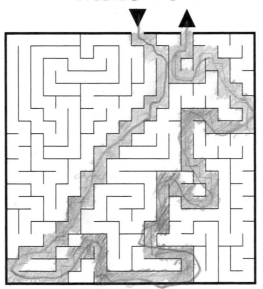

Solutions on
page 302

Maze #6

Solution on page 303

Maze #7

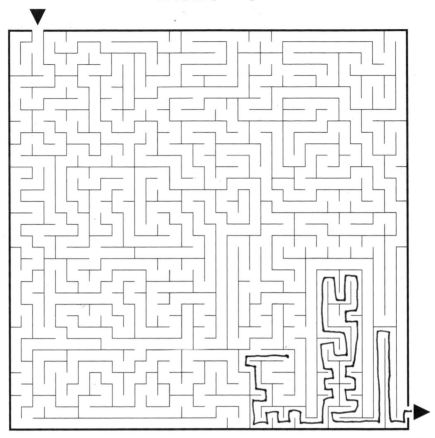

Solution on page 303

Solution on page 303

Solution on page 303

Solution on page 304

Maze #11

Solution on page 304

Maze #12

Solution on page 304

Solution on page 304

Solution on page 305

Solution on page 305

Solution on page 305

Maze #17

Solution on page 305

Maze #18

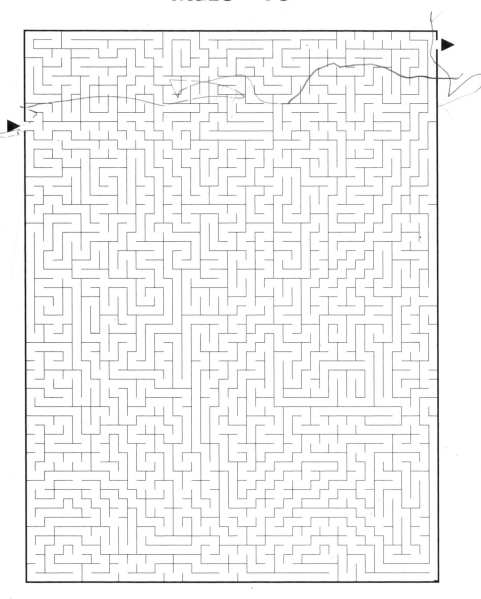

Solution on page 306

Maze #19

Solution on page 306

Maze #20

Solution on page 306

Solution on page 306

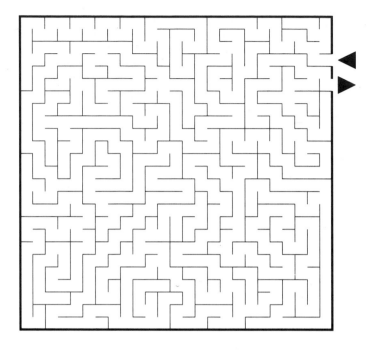

Solution on page 307

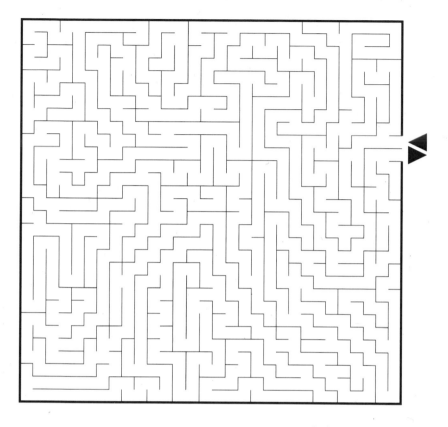

Solution on page 307

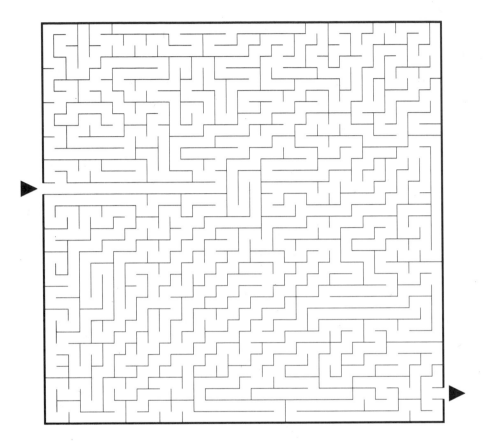

Solution on page 307

Maze #25

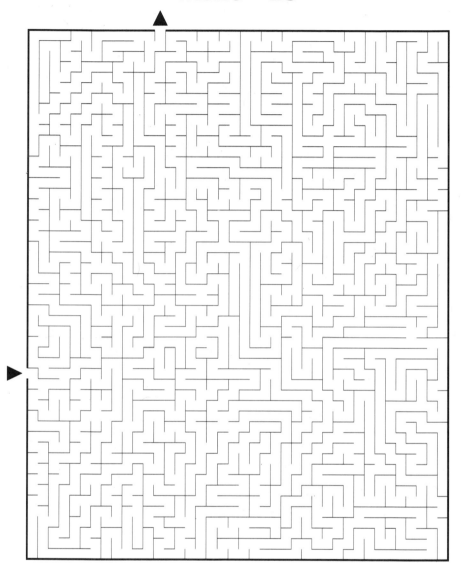

Solution on page 307

Maze #26

Solution on page 307

Maze #27

Solution on page 308

Maze #28

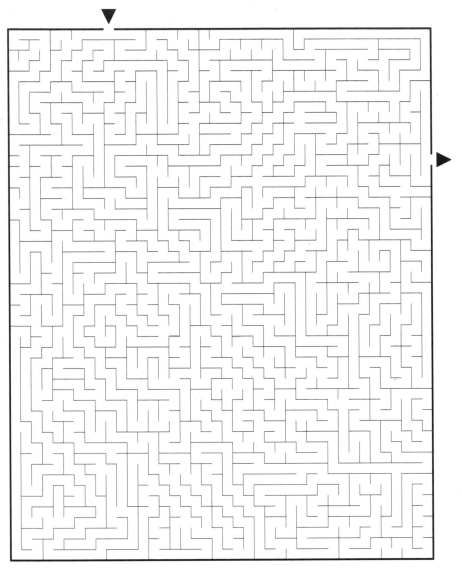

Solution on page 308

Maze #29

Solution on page 308

Solution on page 308

Solution on page 309

Maze #32

Solution on page 309

Maze #33

Solution on page 309

Solution on page 309

Solution on page 310

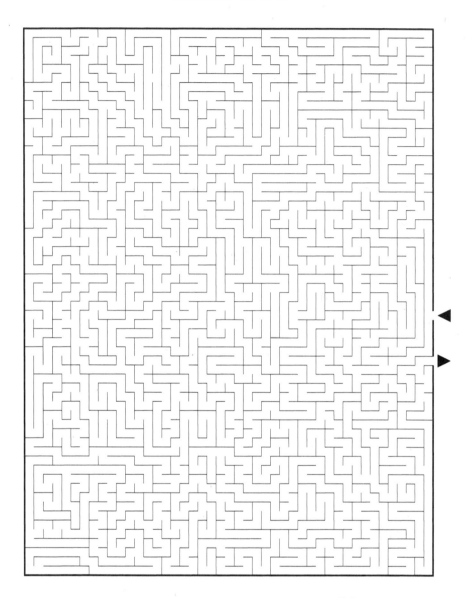

Solution on page 310

Maze #37

Solution on page 310

Maze #38

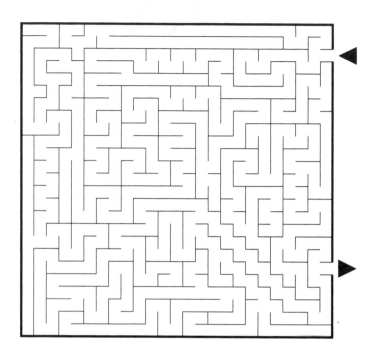

Maze #39

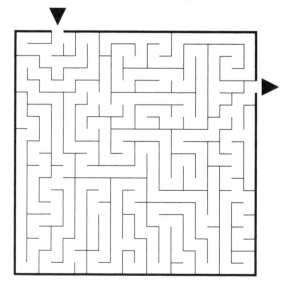

*Solutions on
page 310*

Maze #40

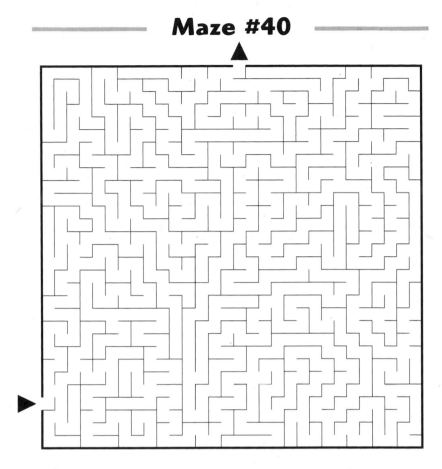

Solution on page 311

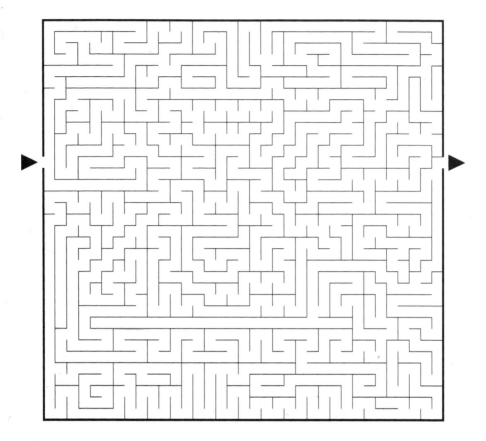

Solution on page 311

Solution on page 311

Maze #43

Solution on page 311

Maze #44

Solution on page 311

Maze #45

Solution on page 312

Solution on page 312

Solution on page 312

Maze #48

Solution on page 313

Solution on page 313

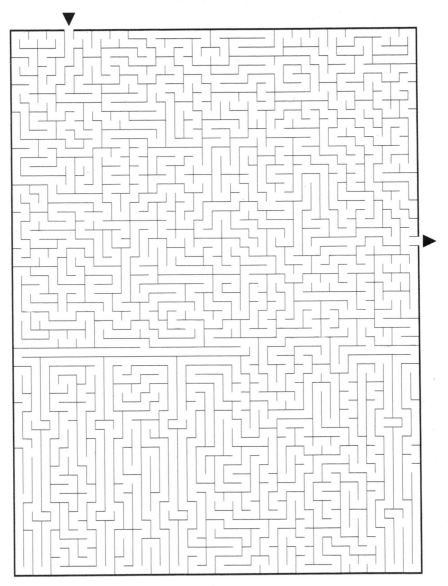

Solution on page 314

Solution on page 314

Solution on page 314

Solution on page 314

Solution on page 315

Solution on page 315

Maze #56

Solution on page 315

Solution on page 316

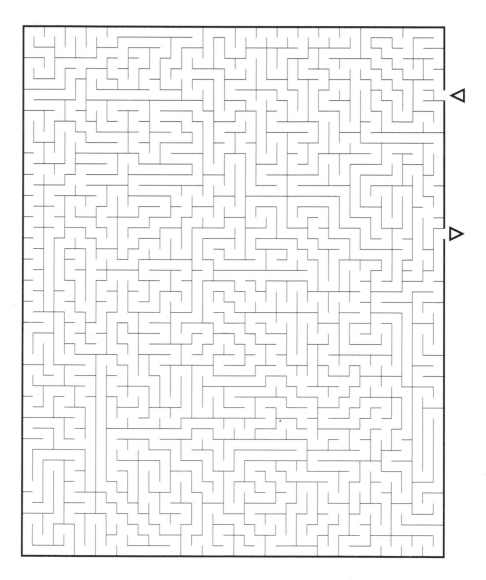

Solution on page 316

R This is a reversed maze. After you have traced the true path (solution) lightly in pencil, color in all the wrong paths with a thick pen or pencil to create your picture.

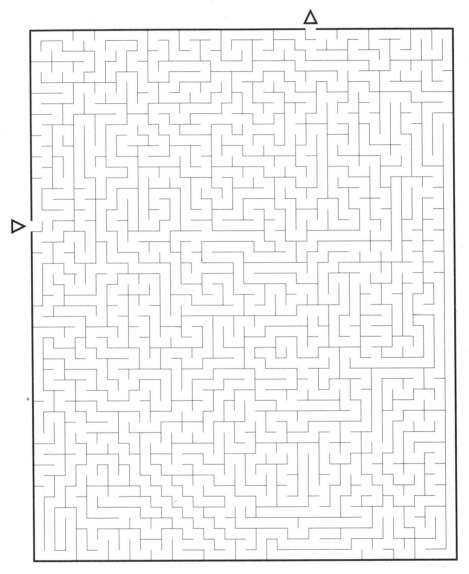

Solution on page 316

R This is a reversed maze. After you have traced the true path (solution) lightly in pencil, color in all the wrong paths with a thick pen or pencil to create your picture.

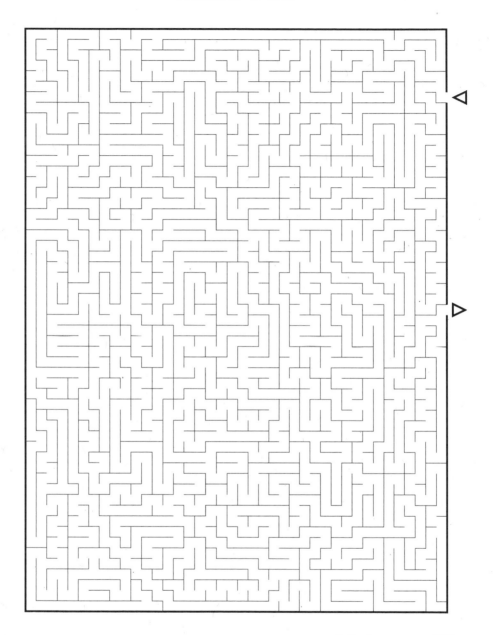

Solution on page 317

R This is a reversed maze. After you have traced the true path (solution) lightly in pencil, color in all the wrong paths with a thick pen or pencil to create your picture.

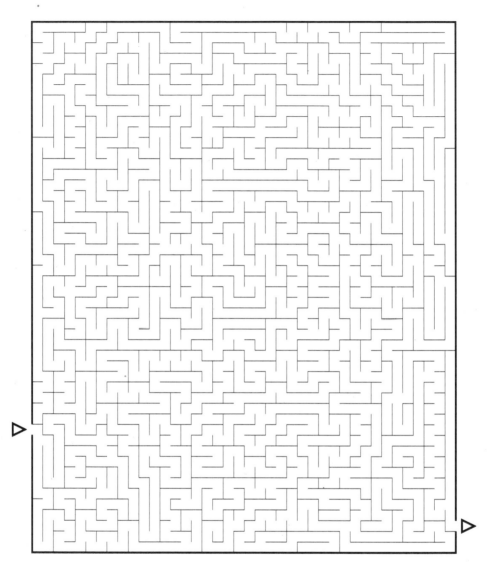

Solution on page 317

R This is a reversed maze. After you have traced the true path (solution) lightly in pencil, color in all the wrong paths with a thick pen or pencil to create your picture.

Solution on page 317

R This is a reversed maze. After you have traced the true path (solution) lightly in pencil, color in all the wrong paths with a thick pen or pencil to create your picture.

Solution on page 318

 This is a reversed maze. After you have traced the true path (solution) lightly in pencil, color in all the wrong paths with a thick pen or pencil to create your picture.

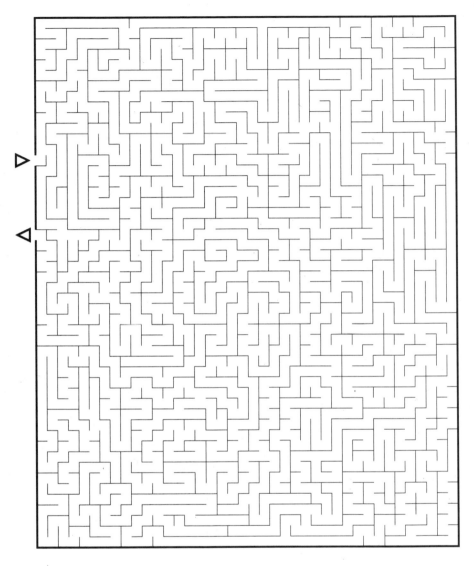

Solution on page 318

R This is a reversed maze. After you have traced the true path (solution) lightly in pencil, color in all the wrong paths with a thick pen or pencil to create your picture.

Solution on page 318

R This is a reversed maze. After you have traced the true path (solution) lightly in pencil, color in all the wrong paths with a thick pen or pencil to create your picture.

Maze #66

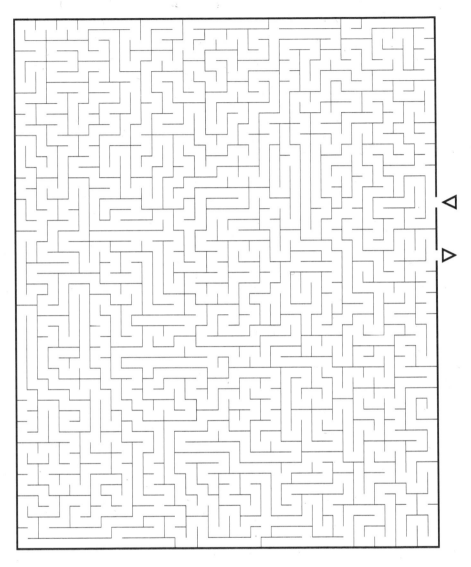

Solution on page 319

R This is a reversed maze. After you have traced the true path (solution) lightly in pencil, color in all the wrong paths with a thick pen or pencil to create your picture.

Maze #67

Solution on page 319

R This is a reversed maze. After you have traced the true path (solution) lightly in pencil, color in all the wrong paths with a thick pen or pencil to create your picture.

Maze #68

Solution on page 319

R This is a reversed maze. After you have traced the true path (solution) lightly in pencil, color in all the wrong paths with a thick pen or pencil to create your picture.

Solution on page 320

R This is a reversed maze. After you have traced the true path (solution) lightly in pencil, color in all the wrong paths with a thick pen or pencil to create your picture.

Solution on page 320

R This is a reversed maze. After you have traced the true path (solution) lightly in pencil, color in all the wrong paths with a thick pen or pencil to create your picture.

Maze #71

Solution on page 320

R This is a reversed maze. After you have traced the true path (solution) lightly in pencil, color in all the wrong paths with a thick pen or pencil to create your picture.

Solution on page 320

R This is a reversed maze. After you have traced the true path (solution) lightly in pencil, color in all the wrong paths with a thick pen or pencil to create your picture.

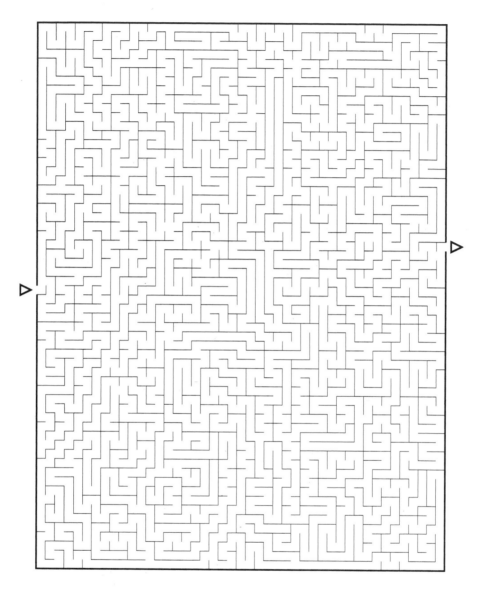

Solution on page 321

R This is a reversed maze. After you have traced the true path (solution) lightly in pencil, color in all the wrong paths with a thick pen or pencil to create your picture.

Solution on page 321

R This is a reversed maze. After you have traced the true path (solution) lightly in pencil, color in all the wrong paths with a thick pen or pencil to create your picture.

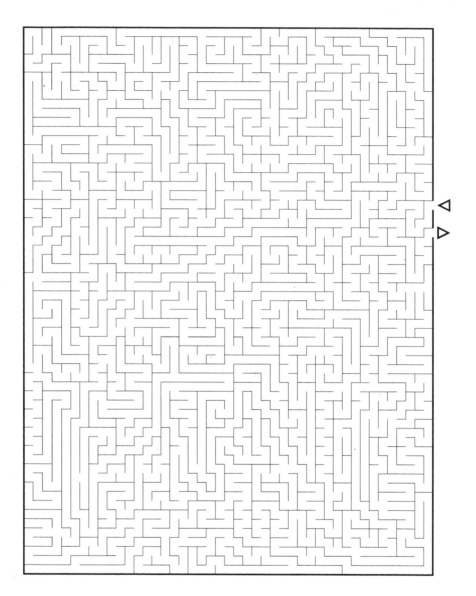

Solution on page 321

R This is a reversed maze. After you have traced the true path (solution) lightly in pencil, color in all the wrong paths with a thick pen or pencil to create your picture.

Maze #76

Solution on page 321

R This is a reversed maze. After you have traced the true path (solution) lightly in pencil, color in all the wrong paths with a thick pen or pencil to create your picture.

Maze #77

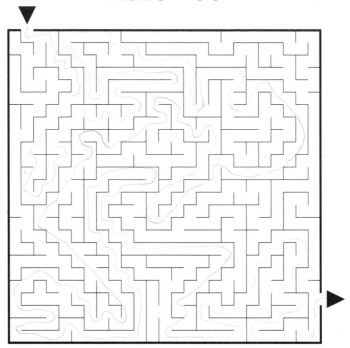

Maze #78

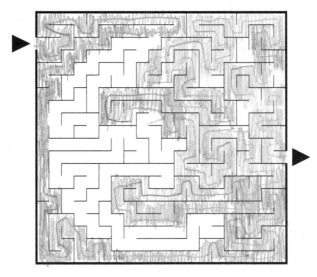

Solutions on page 322

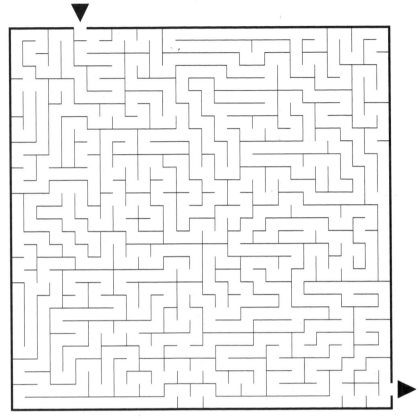

Solution on page 322

Solution on page 322

Solution on page 322

Solution on page 323

Maze #83

Solution on page 323

Maze #84

Solution on page 323

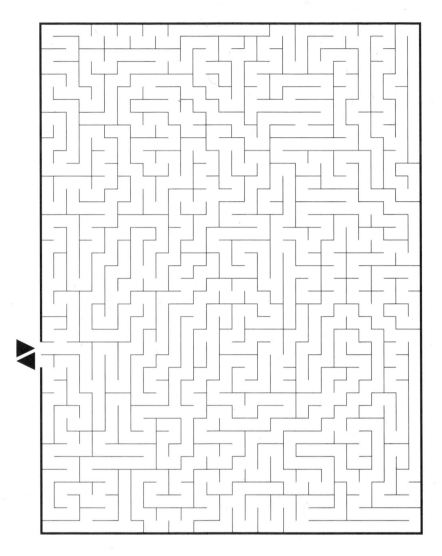

Solution on page 323

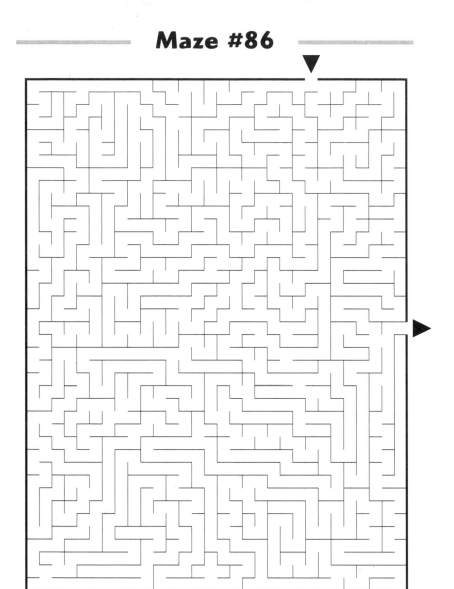

Solution on page 324

Maze #87

Solution on page 324

Solution on page 324

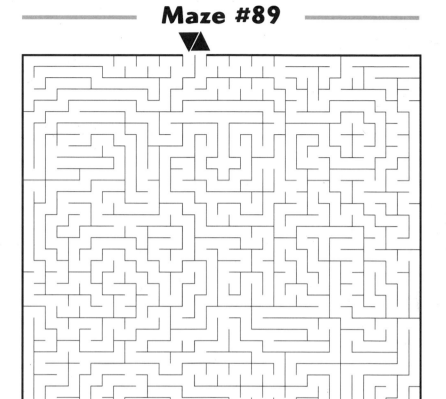

Solution on page 324

Solution on page 325

Solution on page 325

Solution on page 325

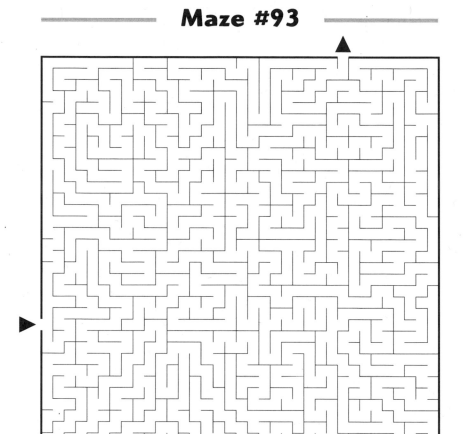

Solution on page 325

Maze #94

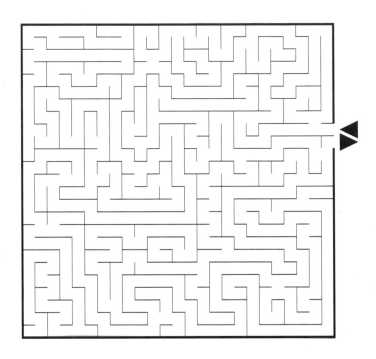

Maze #95

Solutions on page 326

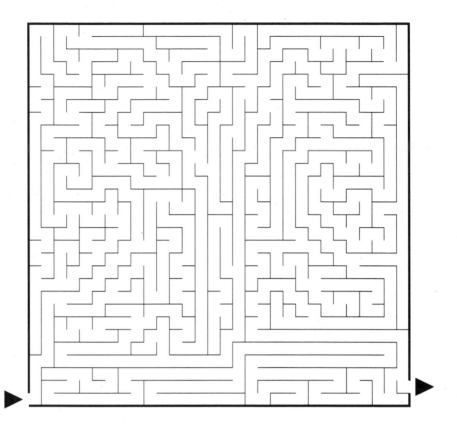

Solution on page 326

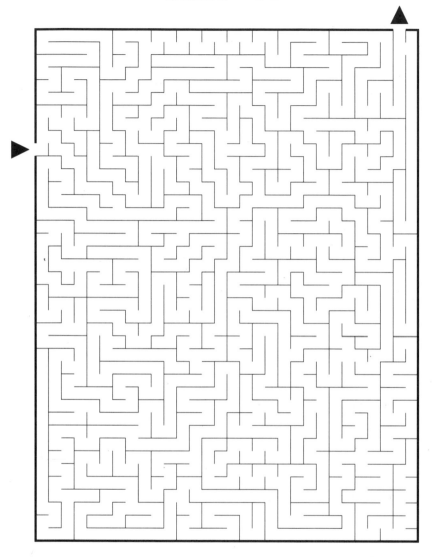

Solution on page 326

Maze #98

Solution on page 326

Maze #99

Solution on page 327

Solution on page 327

Solution on page 327

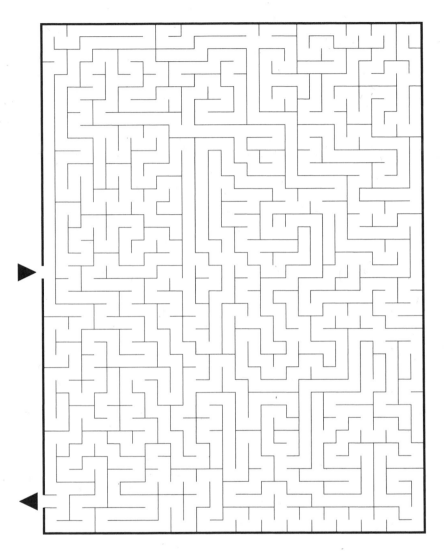

Solution on page 327

Maze #103

Solution on page 328

Solution on page 328

Maze #105

Solution on page 328

Solution on page 329

Maze #108

Solution on page 329

Solution on page 329

Maze #110

Solution on page 329

Maze #111

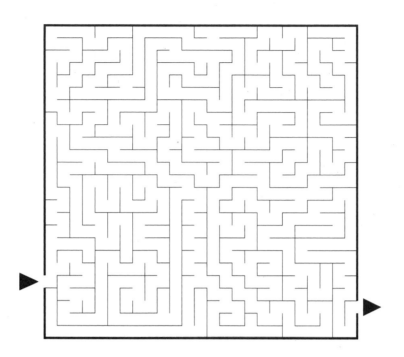

Maze #112

Solutions on page 330

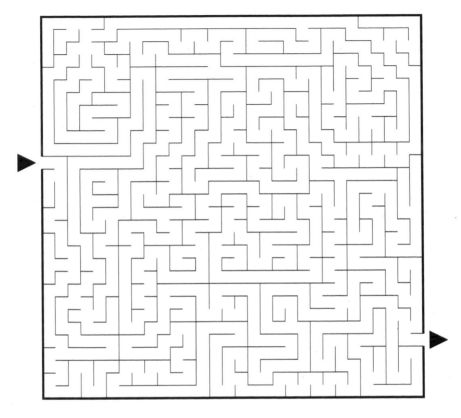

Solution on page 330

Solution on page 330

Solution on page 330

Maze #116

Solution on page 331

Maze #117

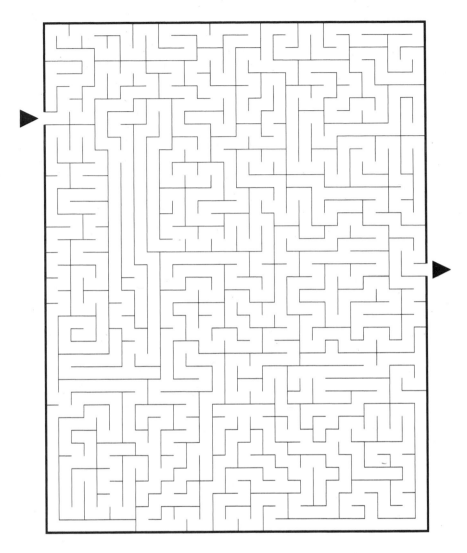

Solution on page 331

Maze #118

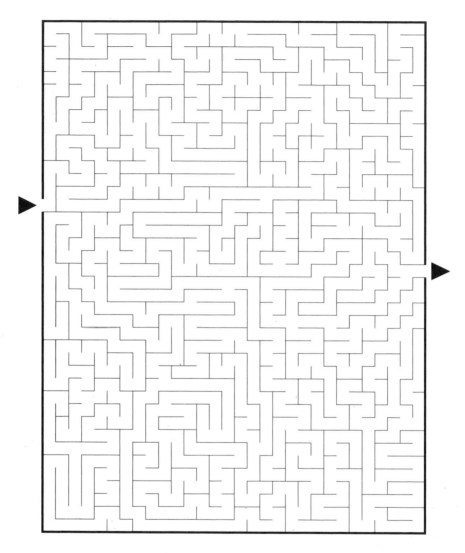

Solution on page 331

Solution on page 331

Solution on page 332

Solution on page 332

Solution on page 332

Solution on page 332

Solution on page 333

Solution on page 333

Solution on page 333

Solution on page 333

Solution on page 334

Maze #129

Solution on page 334

Maze #130

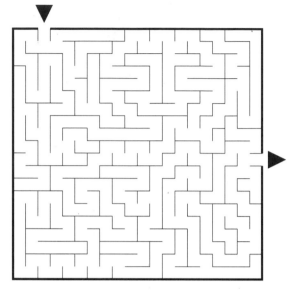

Maze #131

Solutions on page 334

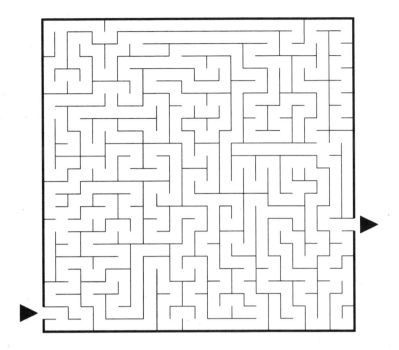

Solution on page 334

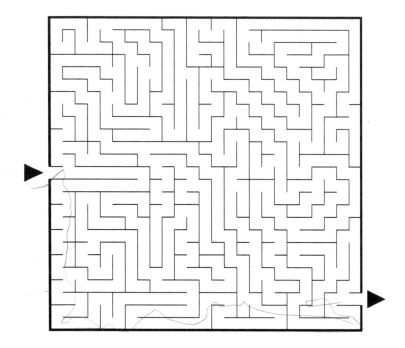

Solution on page 335

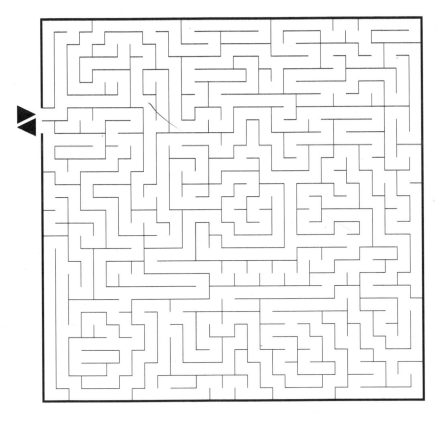

Solution on page 335

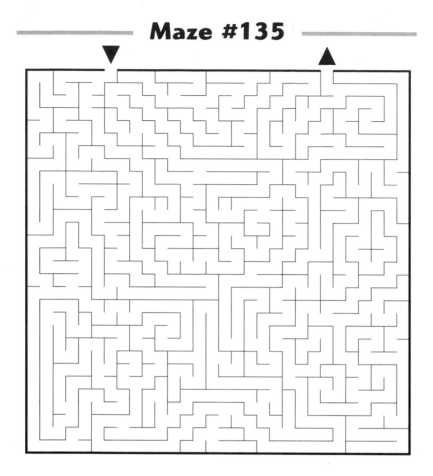

Solution on page 335

Solution on page 335

Solution on page 335

Solution on page 336

Solution on page 336

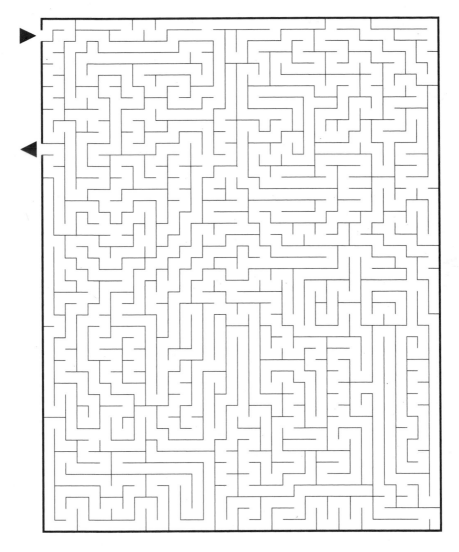

Solution on page 336

Solution on page 336

Solution on page 337

Maze #143

Solution on page 337

Solution on page 337

Solution on page 338

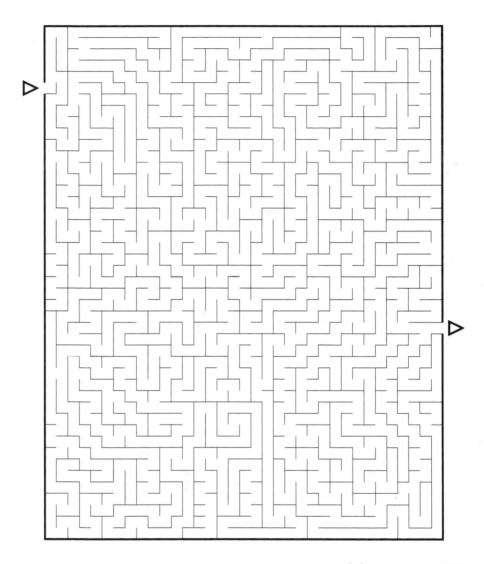

Solution on page 338

R This is a reversed maze. After you have traced the true path (solution) lightly in pencil, color in all the wrong paths with a thick pen or pencil to create your picture.

Solution on page 338

R This is a reversed maze. After you have traced the true path (solution) lightly in pencil, color in all the wrong paths with a thick pen or pencil to create your picture.

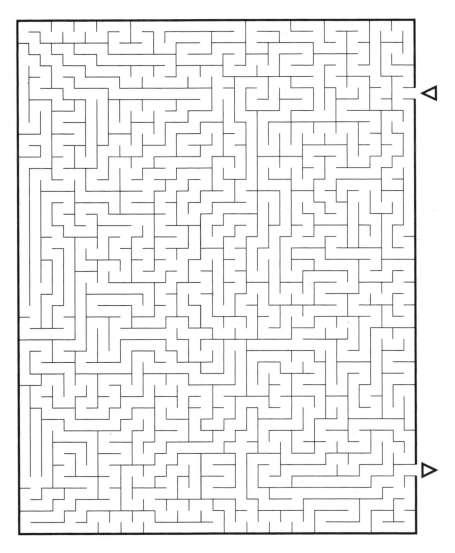

Solution on page 339

R This is a reversed maze. After you have traced the true path (solution) lightly in pencil, color in all the wrong paths with a thick pen or pencil to create your picture.

Solution on page 339

R This is a reversed maze. After you have traced the true path (solution) lightly in pencil, color in all the wrong paths with a thick pen or pencil to create your picture.

Solution on page 339

R This is a reversed maze. After you have traced the true path (solution) lightly in pencil, color in all the wrong paths with a thick pen or pencil to create your picture.

Maze #151

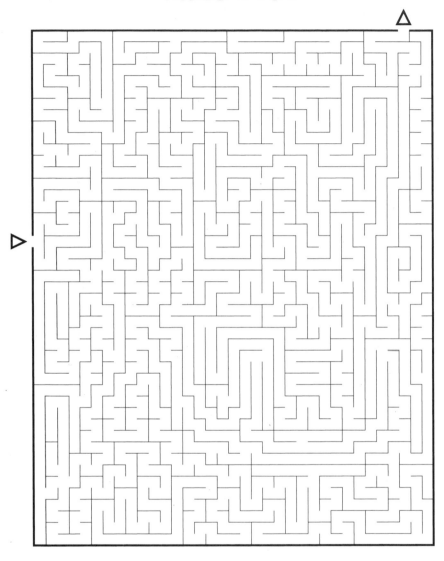

Solution on page 340

R This is a reversed maze. After you have traced the true path (solution) lightly in pencil, color in all the wrong paths with a thick pen or pencil to create your picture.

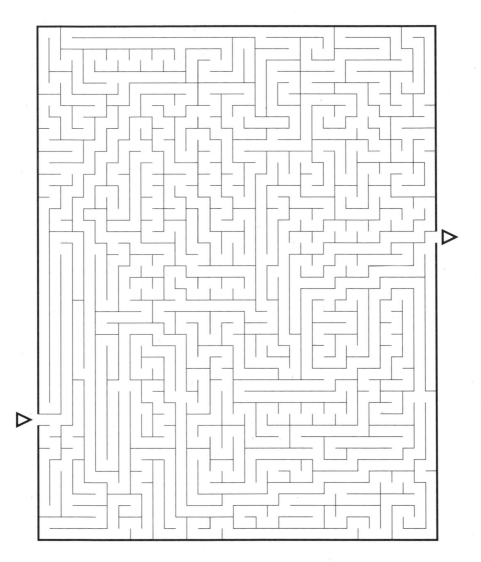

Solution on page 340

R This is a reversed maze. After you have traced the true path (solution) lightly in pencil, color in all the wrong paths with a thick pen or pencil to create your picture.

Maze #153

Solution on page 340

R This is a reversed maze. After you have traced the true path (solution) lightly in pencil, color in all the wrong paths with a thick pen or pencil to create your picture.

Maze #154

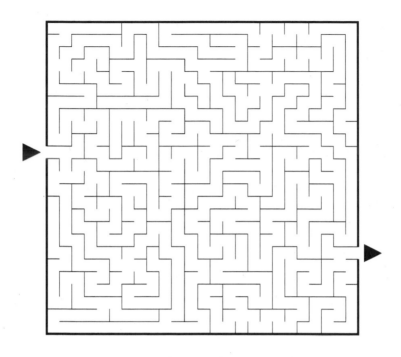

Maze #155

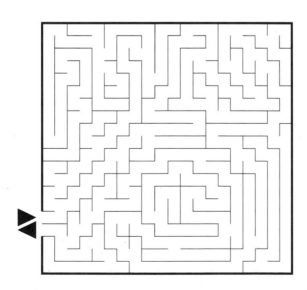

Solutions on page 341

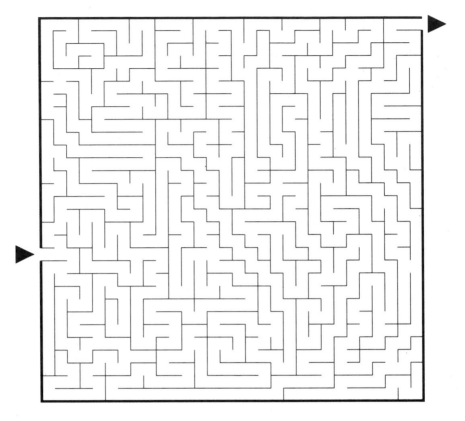

Solution on page 341

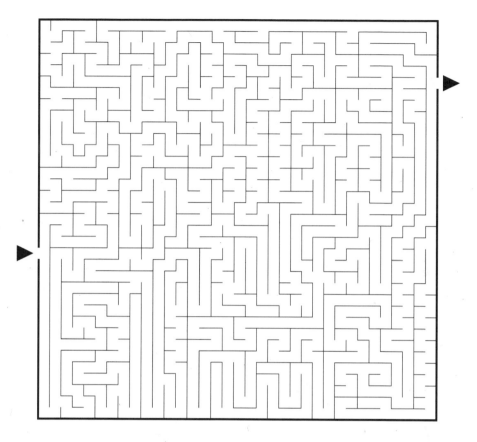

Solution on page 341

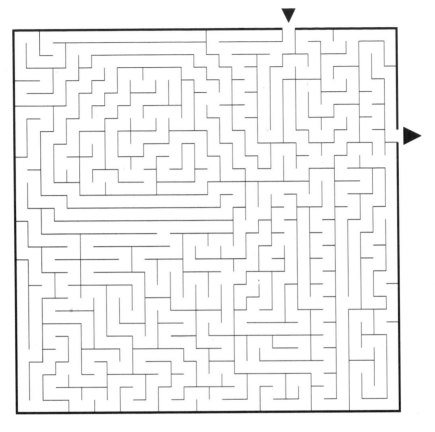

Solution on page 341

Maze #159

Solution on page 342

Maze #160

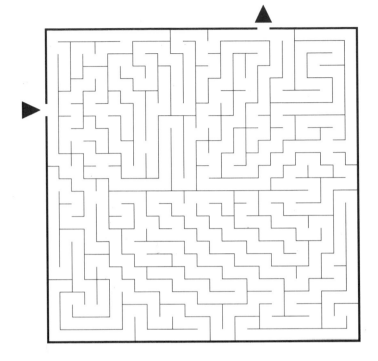

Maze #161

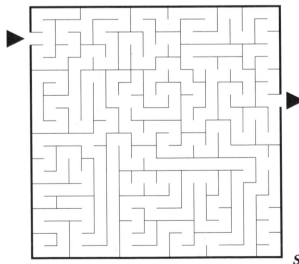

Solutions on page 342

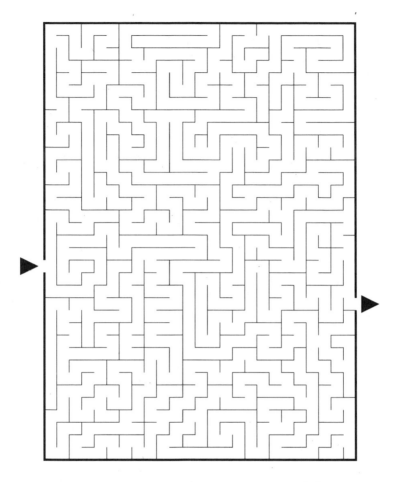

Solution on page 342

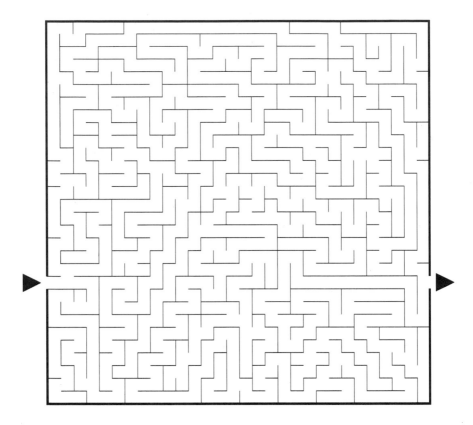

Solution on page 342

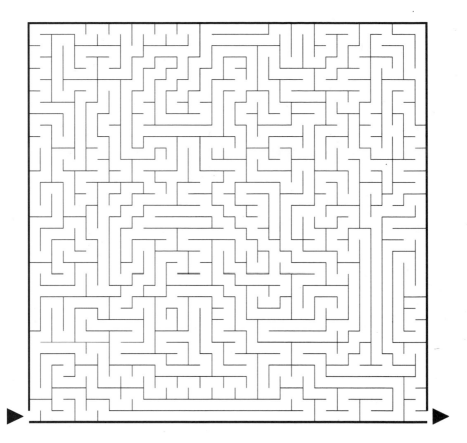

Solution on page 343

Solution on page 343

Solution on page 343

Maze #167

Solution on page 343

Solution on page 344

Solution on page 344

Solution on page 344

Solution on page 344

Solution on page 345

Solution on page 345

Solution on page 345

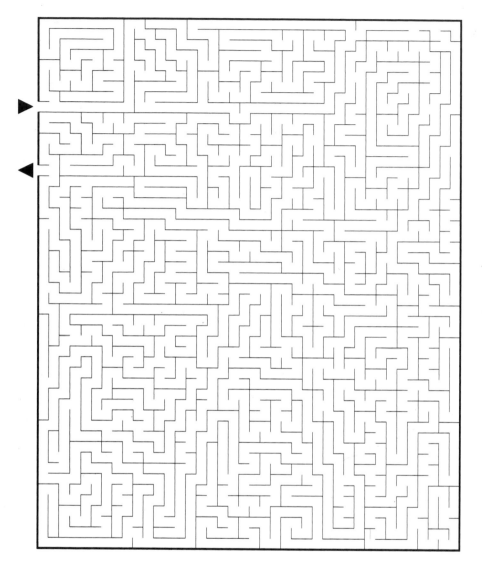

Solution on page 345

Solution on page 346

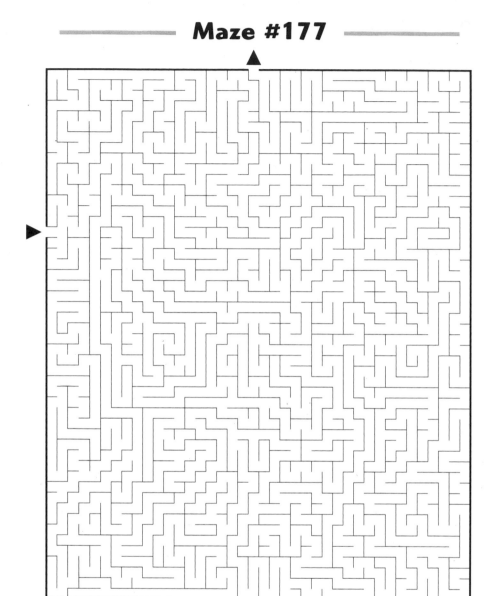

Solution on page 346

Solution on page 346

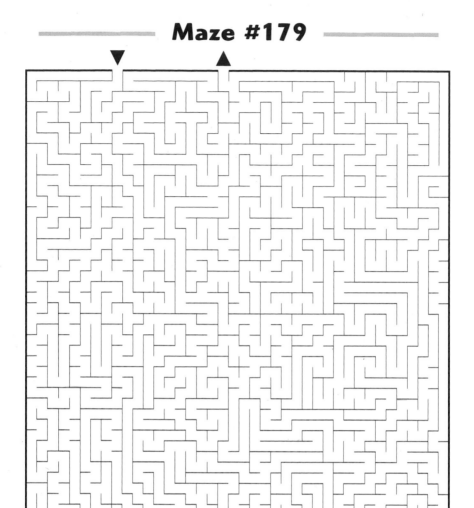

Solution on page 346

Solution on page 347

▼ ▲

Solution on page 347

Solution on page 347

Solution on page 347

Solution on page 348

Solution on page 348

Solution on page 348

Solution on page 348

Solution on page 349

Solution on page 349

Maze #190

Solution on page 349

Solution on page 349

Solution on page 350

Solution on page 350

Solution on page 350

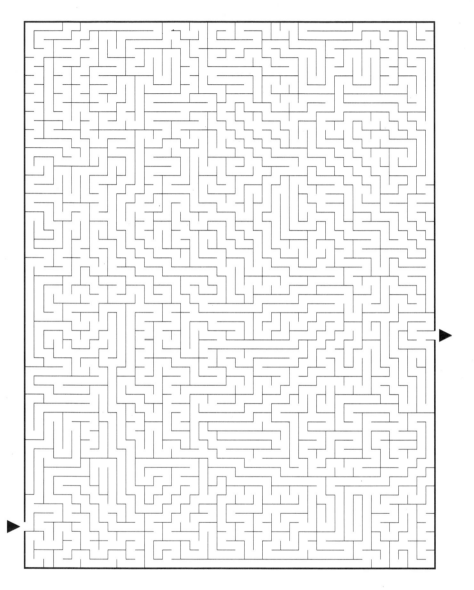

Solution on page 350

Maze #196

Solution on page 351

Solution on page 351

Maze #198

Solution on page 351

Solution on page 351

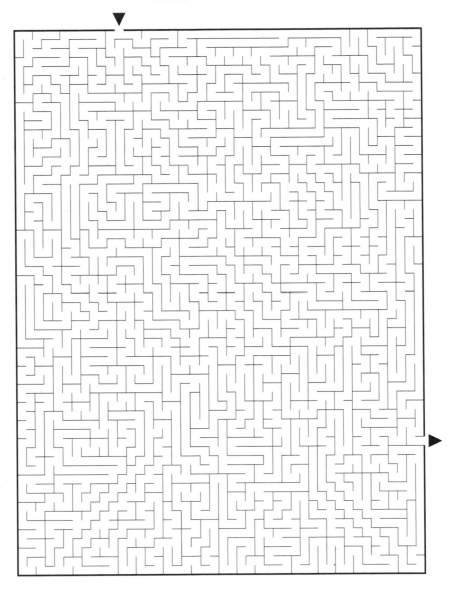

Solution on page 352

Solution on page 352

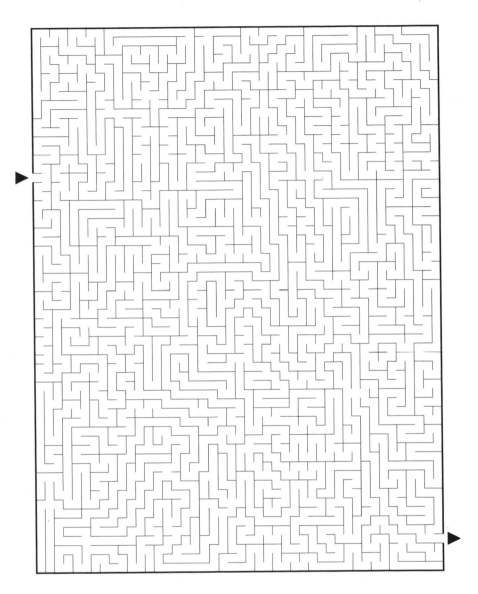

Solution on page 352

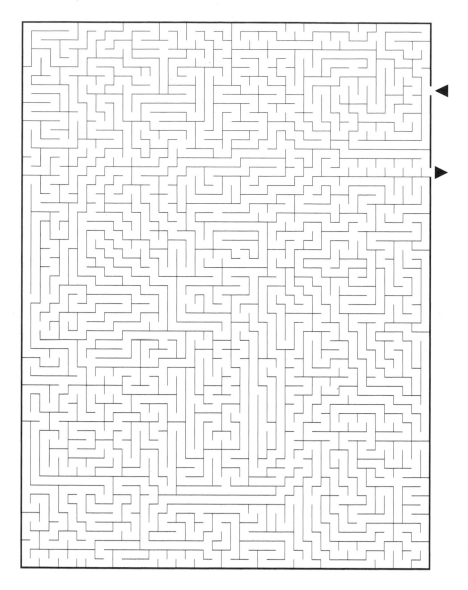

Solution on page 352

Solution on page 353

Solution on page 353

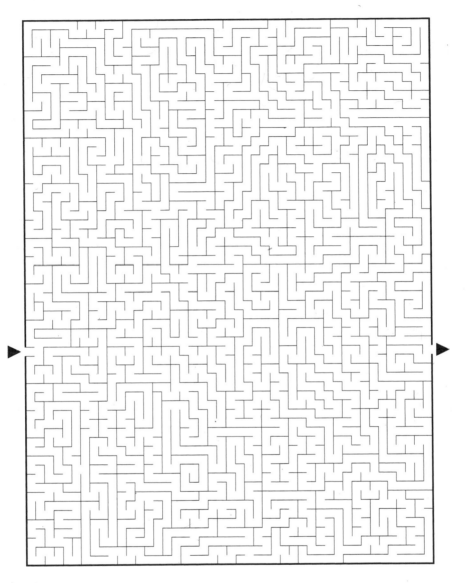

Solution on page 353

Solution on page 353

Solution on page 354

Solution on page 354

Solution on page 354

Solution on page 354

Solution on page 355

Solution on page 355

Solution on page 355

Solution on page 355

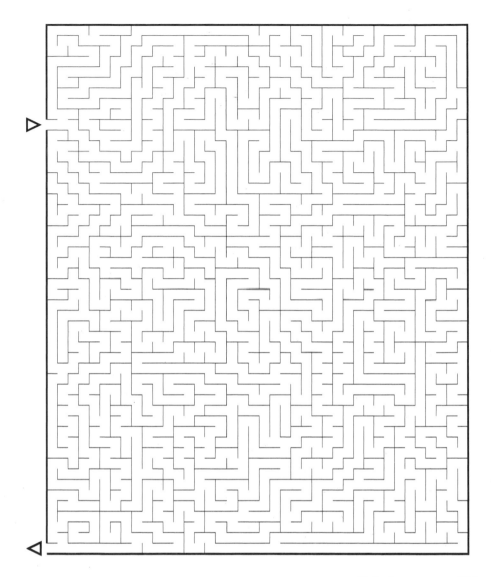

Solution on page 356

R This is a reversed maze. After you have traced the true path (solution) lightly in pencil, color in all the wrong paths with a thick pen or pencil to create your picture.

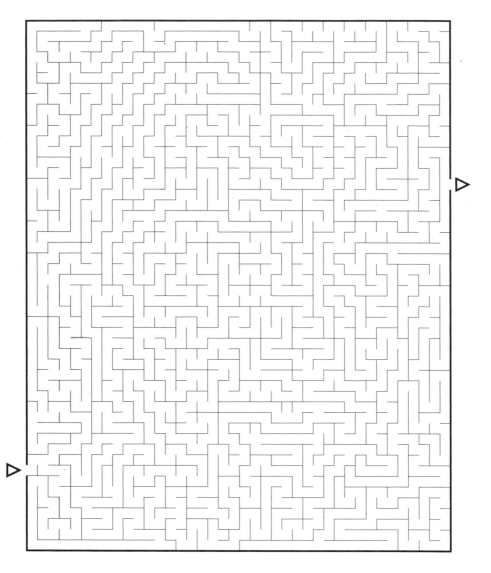

Solution on page 356

R This is a reversed maze. After you have traced the true path (solution) lightly in pencil, color in all the wrong paths with a thick pen or pencil to create your picture.

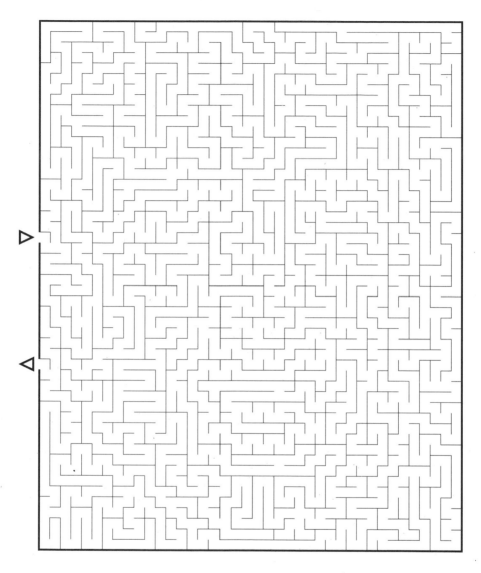

Solution on page 356

R This is a reversed maze. After you have traced the true path (solution) lightly in pencil, color in all the wrong paths with a thick pen or pencil to create your picture.

Maze #219

Solution on page 356

R This is a reversed maze. After you have traced the true path (solution) lightly in pencil, color in all the wrong paths with a thick pen or pencil to create your picture.

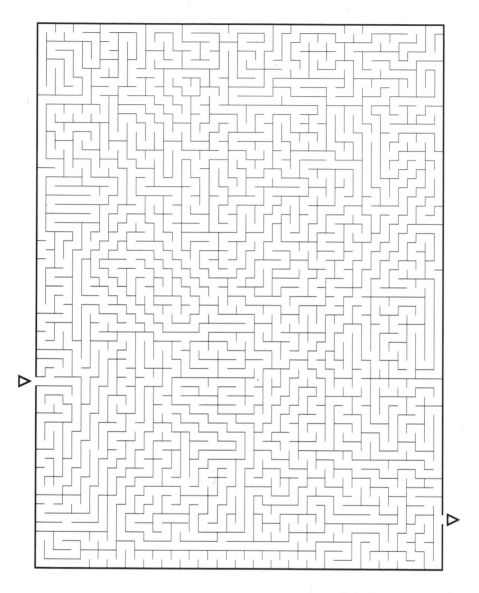

Solution on page 357

R This is a reversed maze. After you have traced the true path (solution) lightly in pencil, color in all the wrong paths with a thick pen or pencil to create your picture.

Maze #221

Solution on page 357

R This is a reversed maze. After you have traced the true path (solution) lightly in pencil, color in all the wrong paths with a thick pen or pencil to create your picture.

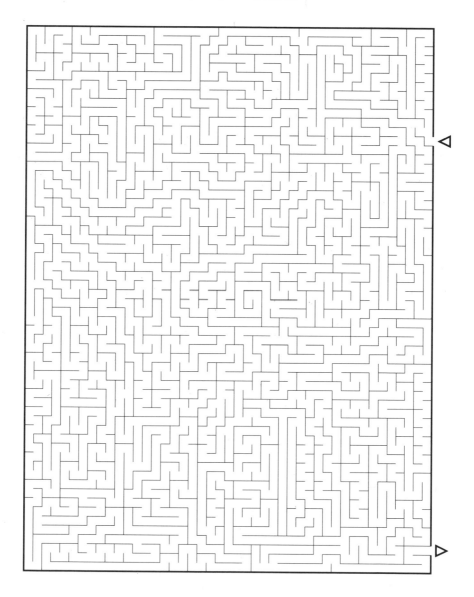

Solution on page 357

R This is a reversed maze. After you have traced the true path (solution) lightly in pencil, color in all the wrong paths with a thick pen or pencil to create your picture.

Solution on page 358

R This is a reversed maze. After you have traced the true path (solution) lightly in pencil, color in all the wrong paths with a thick pen or pencil to create your picture.

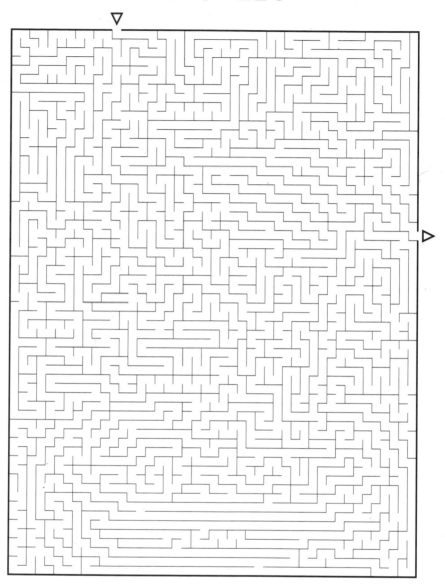

Solution on page 358

R This is a reversed maze. After you have traced the true path (solution) lightly in pencil, color in all the wrong paths with a thick pen or pencil to create your picture.

Solution on page 358

R This is a reversed maze. After you have traced the true path (solution) lightly in pencil, color in all the wrong paths with a thick pen or pencil to create your picture.

Solution on page 359

R This is a reversed maze. After you have traced the true path (solution) lightly in pencil, color in all the wrong paths with a thick pen or pencil to create your picture.

Maze #227

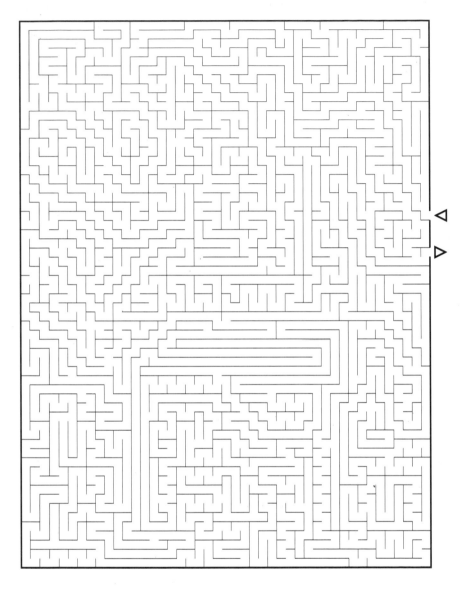

Solution on page 359

R This is a reversed maze. After you have traced the true path (solution) lightly in pencil, color in all the wrong paths with a thick pen or pencil to create your picture.

Solution on page 359

R This is a reversed maze. After you have traced the true path (solution) lightly in pencil, color in all the wrong paths with a thick pen or pencil to create your picture.

Maze #229

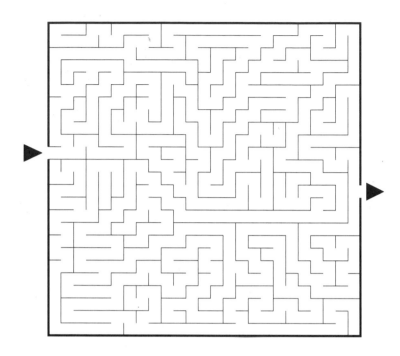

Maze #230

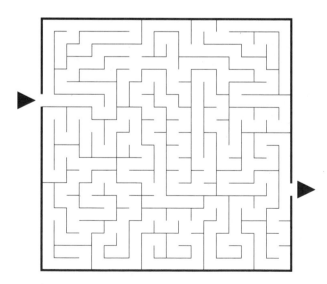

Solutions on page 360

Maze #231

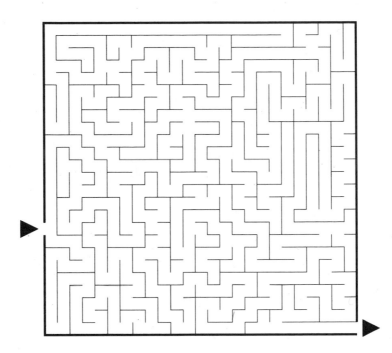

Maze #232

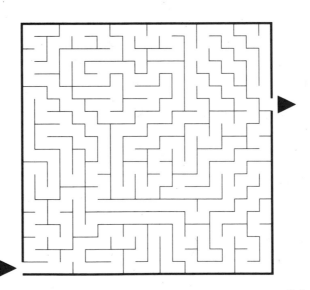

Solutions on page 360

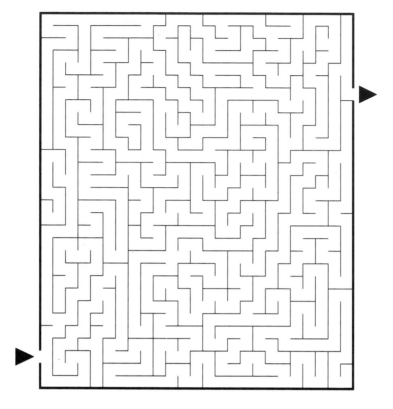

Solution on page 361

Maze #234

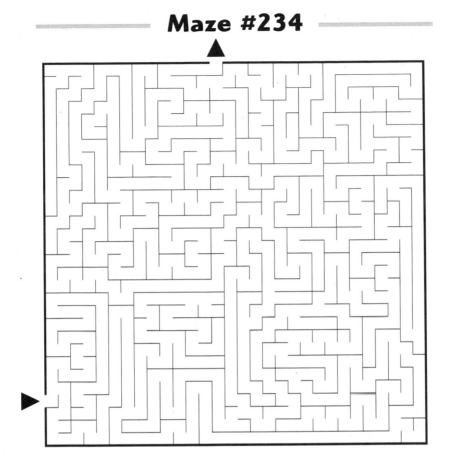

Solution on page 361

Maze #235

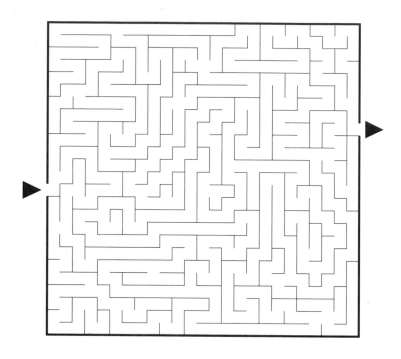

Maze #236

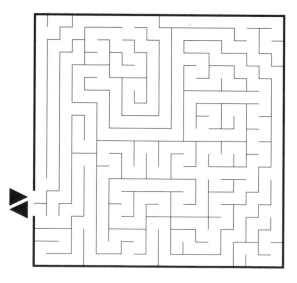

Solutions on page 361

Maze #237

Maze #238

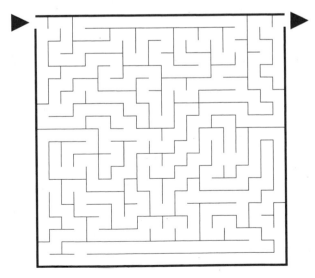

Solutions on page 362

Maze #239

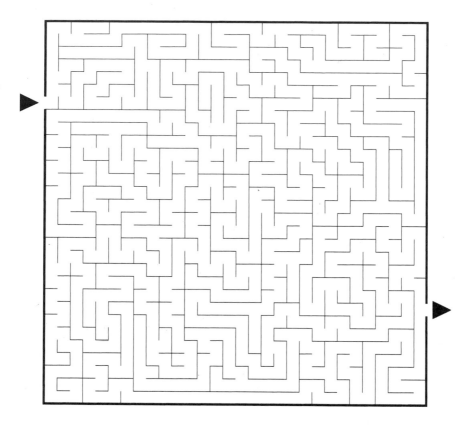

Solution on page 362

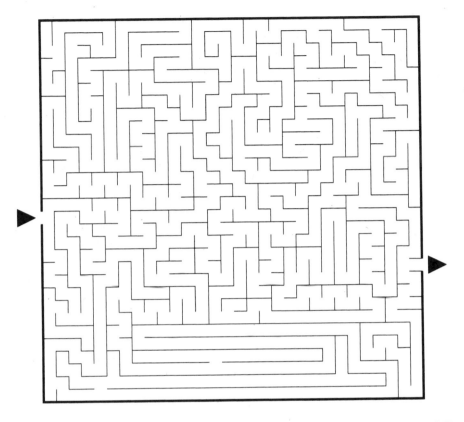

Solution on page 362

Solution on page 363

Solution on page 363

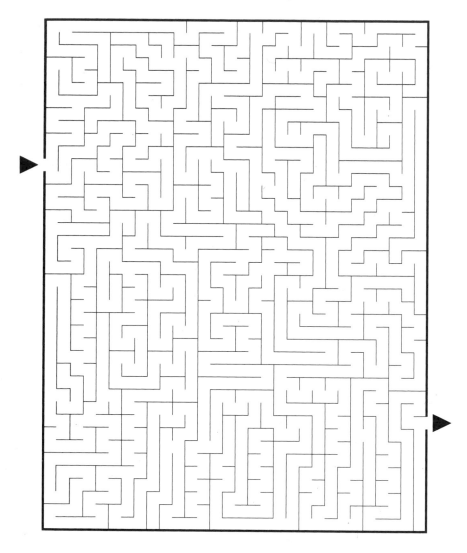

Solution on page 363

Solution on page 364

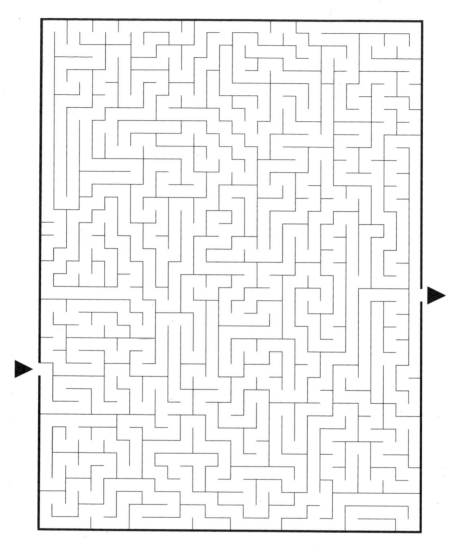

Solution on page 364

Solution on page 364

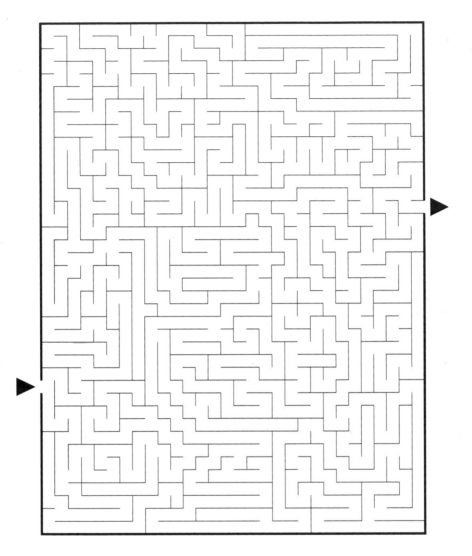

Solution on page 365

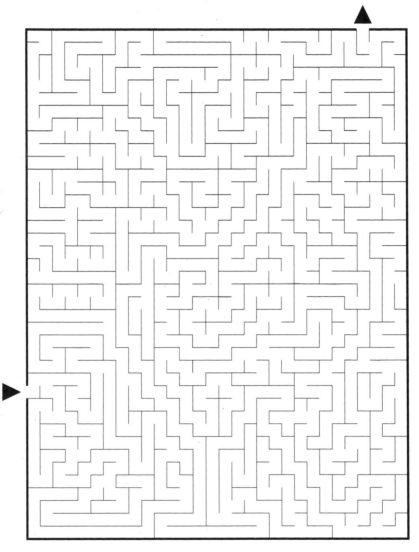

Solution on page 365

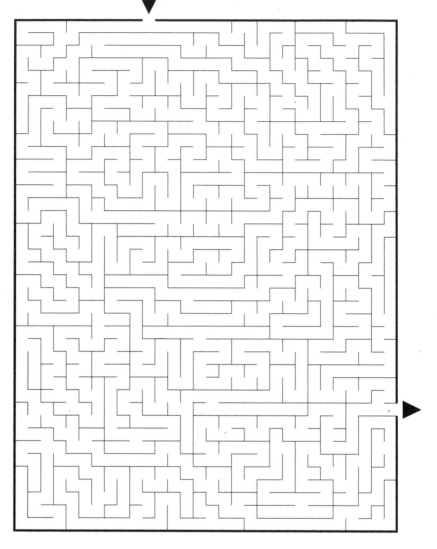

Solution on page 365

Solution on page 366

Solution on page 366

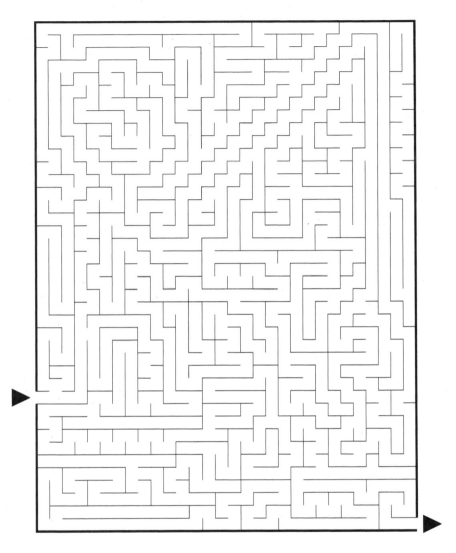

Solution on page 366

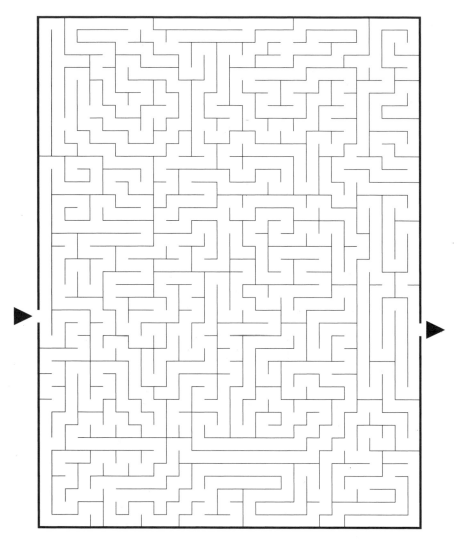

Solution on page 367

Solution on page 367

Solution on page 367

Solution on page 368

Solution on page 368

Solution on page 368

Maze #259

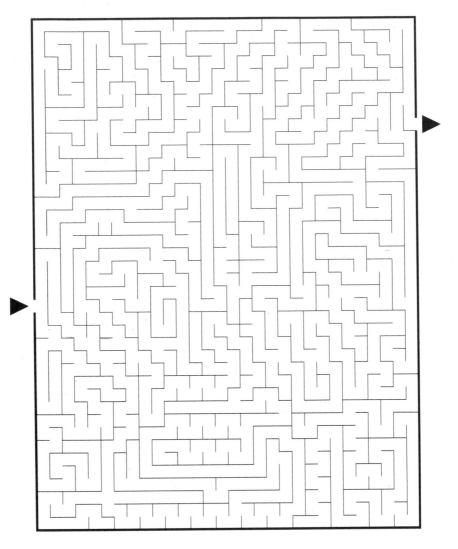

Solution on page 369

Solution on page 369

Maze #261

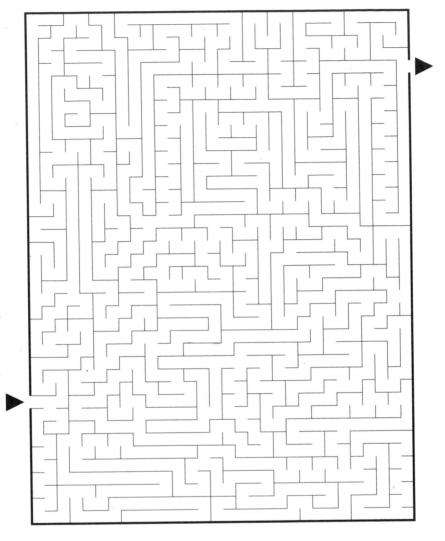

Solution on page 369

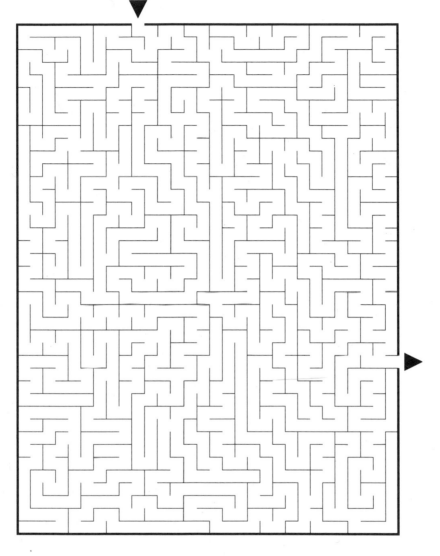

Solution on page 370

Maze #263

Solution on page 370

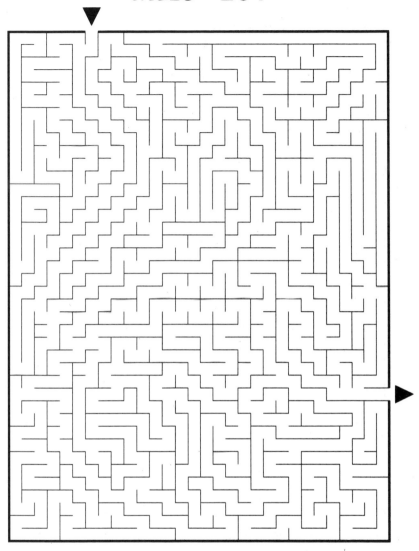

Solution on page 370

Maze #265

Solution on page 371

Solution on page 371

Solution on page 371

Maze #268

Solution on page 372

Solution on page 372

Solution on page 372

Solution on page 373

Maze #272

Solution on page 373

Solution on page 373

Solution on page 374

Solution on page 374

Solution on page 374

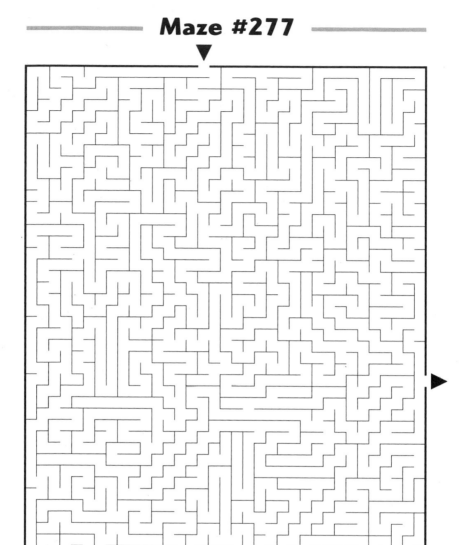

Solution on page 375

Solution on page 375

Solution on page 375

Solution on page 376

Maze #281

Solution on page 376

Solution on page 376

Solution on page 377

Solution on page 377

Maze #285

Solution on page 377

Maze #286

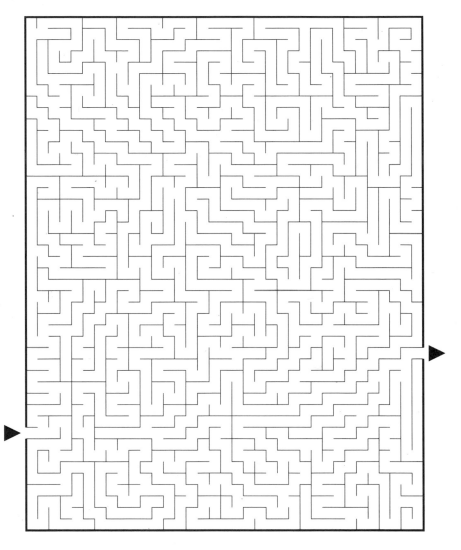

Solution on page 378

Solution on page 378

Solution on page 378

Maze #289

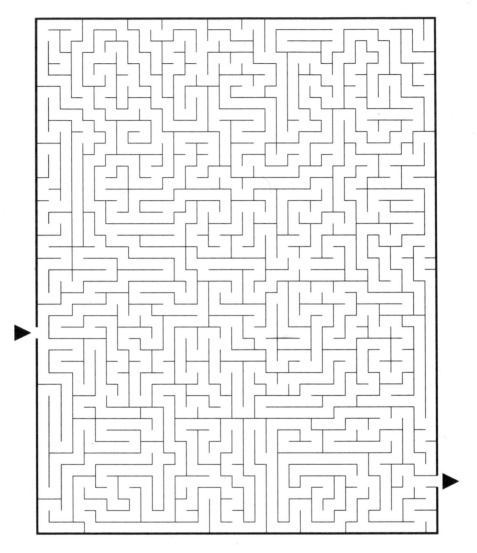

Solution on page 379

Solution on page 379

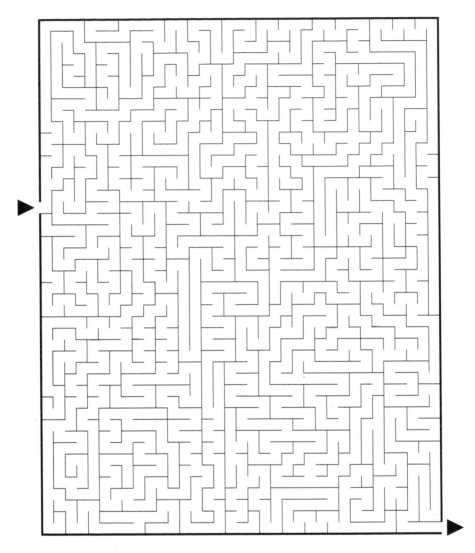

Solution on page 379

Solution on page 380

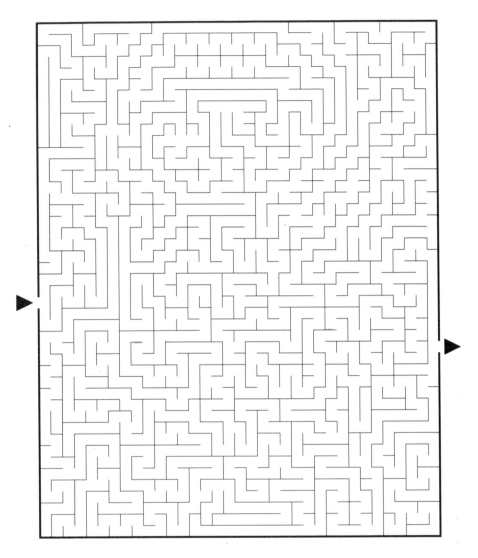

Solution on page 380

Solution on page 380

Solution on page 381

Solution on page 381

Maze #297

Solution on page 381

Maze #298

Solution on page 382

Solution on page 382

Solution on page 382

Solution on page 383

Solution on page 383

Solution on page 383

Solution on page 384

Solution on page 384

SOLUTIONS

Solutions

Maze #1

Maze #3

Maze #2

Maze #4

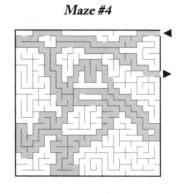

Maze #5

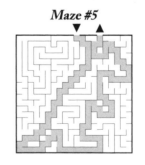

Solutions

Maze #8

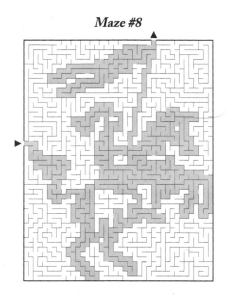

Maze #6

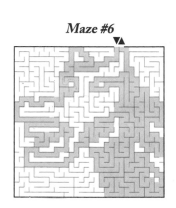

Maze #7

Maze #9

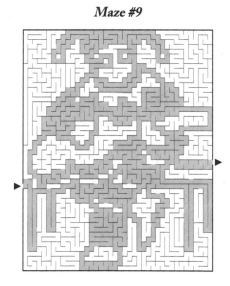

Solutions

Maze #12

Maze #10

Maze #11

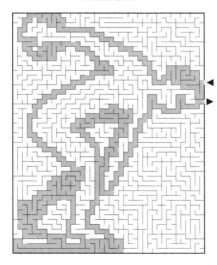

Maze #13

Solutions

Maze #14

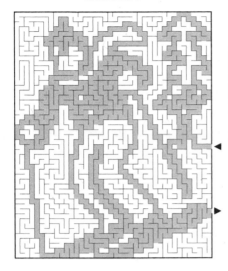

Maze #16

Maze #15

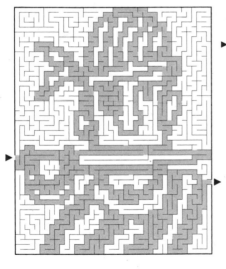

Maze #17

Solutions

Maze #18

Maze #20

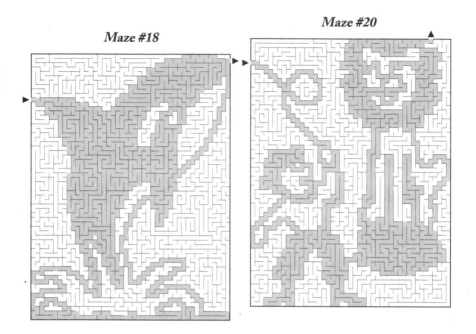

Maze #19

Maze #21

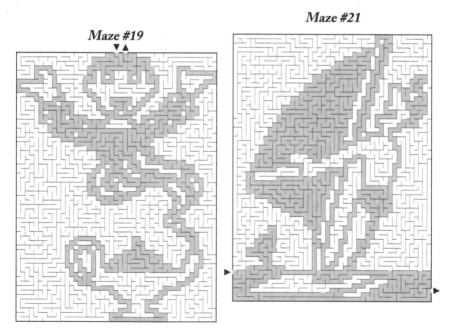

Solutions

Maze #22

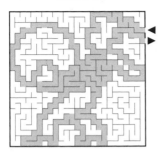

Maze #25

Maze #23

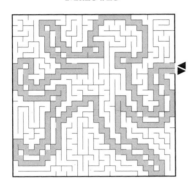

Maze #26

Maze #24

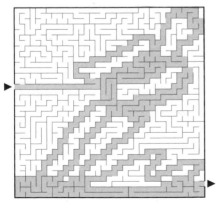

Solutions

Maze #27

Maze #29

Maze #28

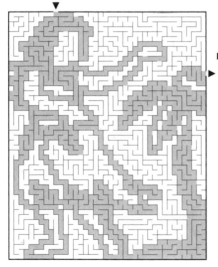

Maze #30

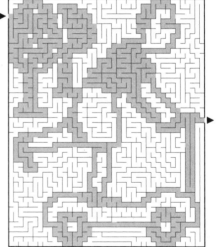

Solutions

Maze #33

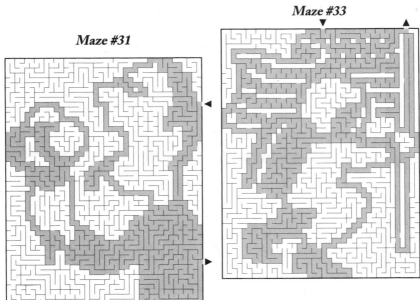

Maze #31

Maze #32

Maze #34

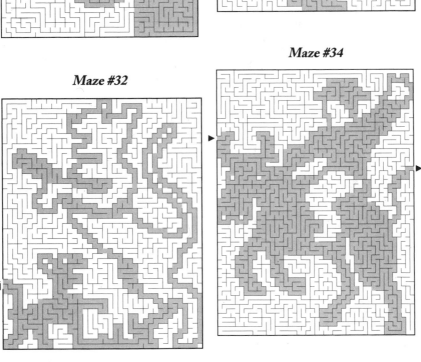

Solutions

Maze #37

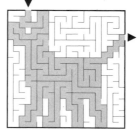

Maze #35

Maze #36

Maze #38

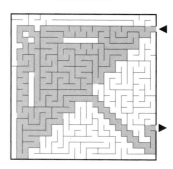

Maze #39

Solutions

Maze #40

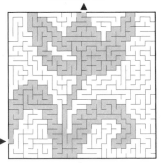

Maze #43

Maze #41

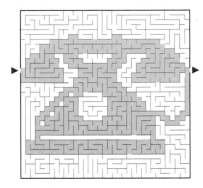

Maze #42

Maze #44

Solutions

Maze #45

Maze #46

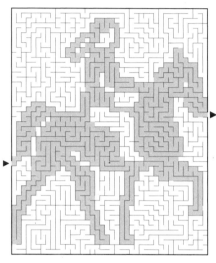

Maze #47

Solutions

Maze #48

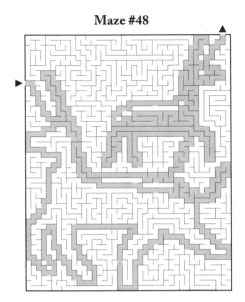

Maze #49

Maze #50

Solutions

Maze #51

Maze #52

Maze #53

Solutions

Maze #54

Maze #55

Maze #56

Solutions

Maze #57

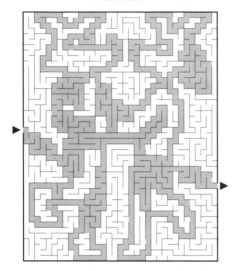

Maze #58

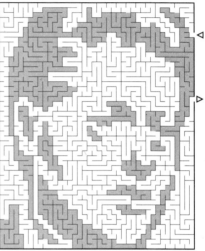

Bill Clinton

Maze #59

Thomas Jefferson

Solutions

Maze #60

Ronald Reagan

Maze #61

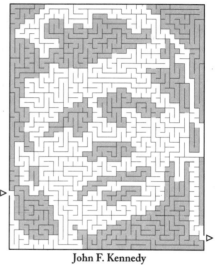

John F. Kennedy

Maze #62

Jimmy Carter

Solutions

Maze #63

Franklin Delano Roosevelt

Maze #64

George W. Bush

Maze #65

Gerald Ford

Solutions

Maze #66

George Washington

Maze #67

Abraham Lincoln

Maze #68

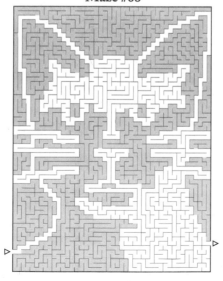

Solutions

Maze #71

Maze #69

Maze #70

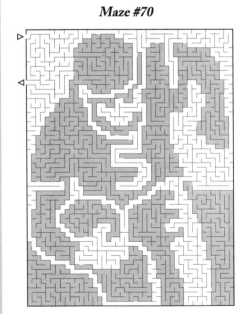

Maze #72

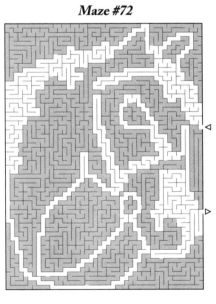

Solutions

Maze #73

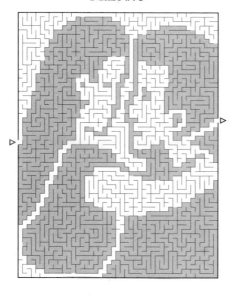

Maze #75

Maze #74

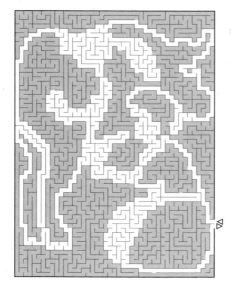

Maze #76

Solutions

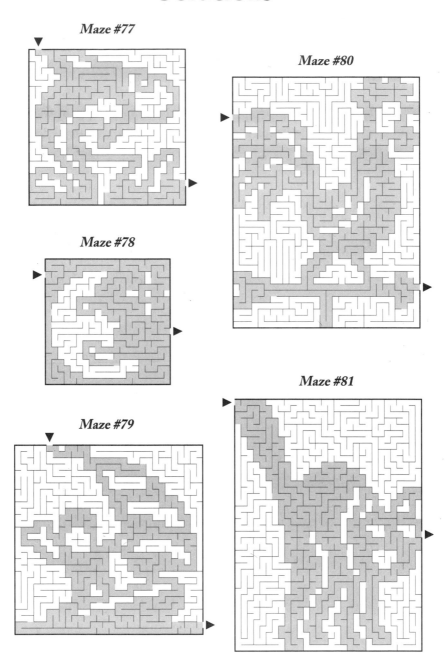

Maze #77

Maze #80

Maze #78

Maze #81

Maze #79

Solutions

Maze #84

Maze #82

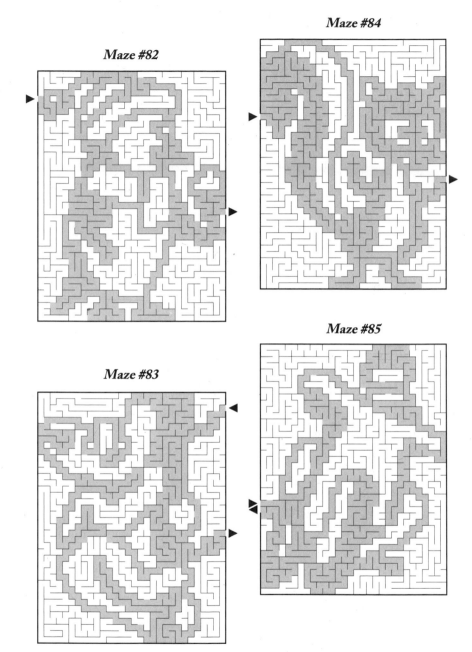

Maze #85

Maze #83

Solutions

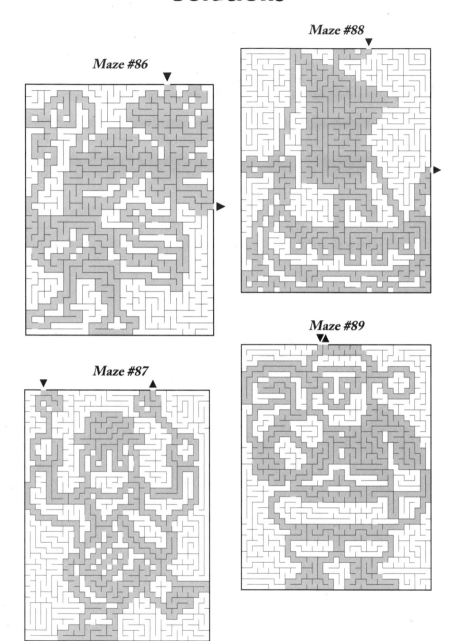

Maze #86

Maze #88

Maze #87

Maze #89

Solutions

Maze #90

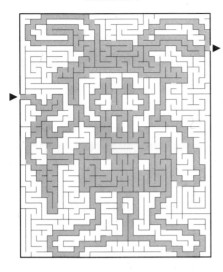

Maze #92

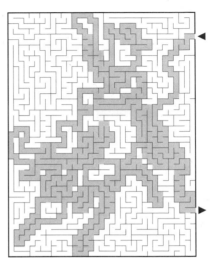

Maze #91

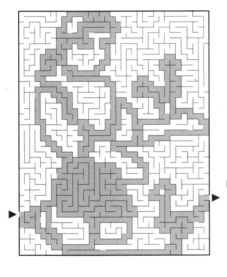

Maze #93

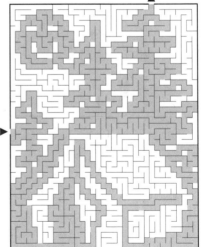

Solutions

Maze #94

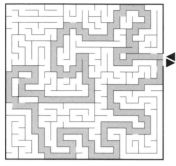

Maze #97

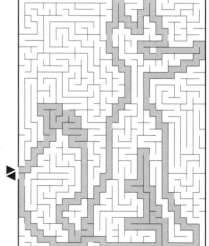

Maze #95

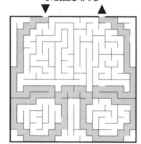

Maze #98

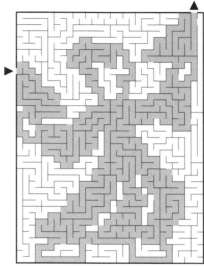

Maze #96

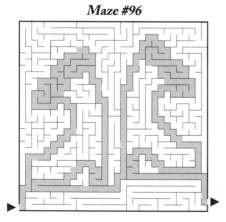

Solutions

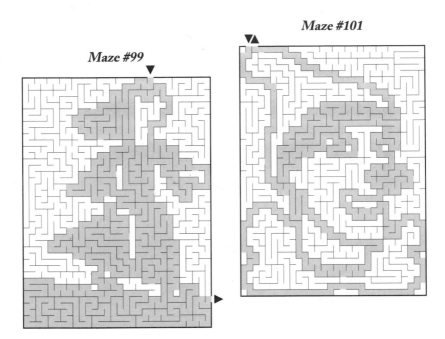

Maze #99

Maze #101

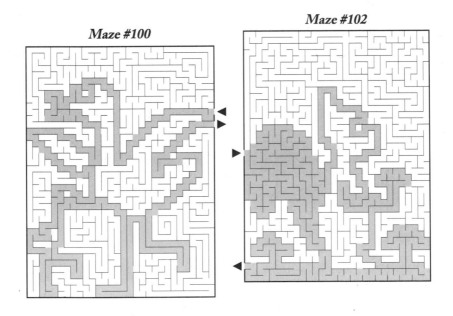

Maze #100

Maze #102

Solutions

Maze #103

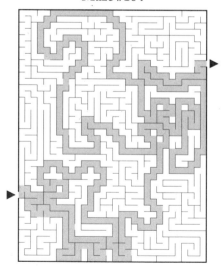

Maze #105

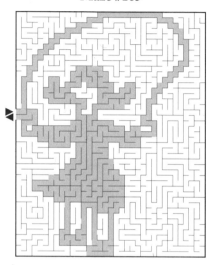

Maze #104

Maze #106

Solutions

Maze #109

Maze #107

Maze #110

Maze #108

Solutions

Maze #111

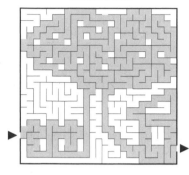

Maze #114

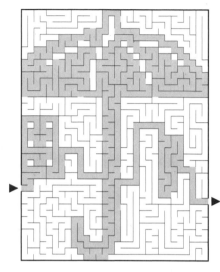

Maze #112

Maze #113

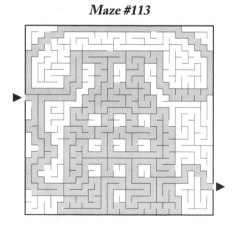

Maze #115

Solutions

Maze #118

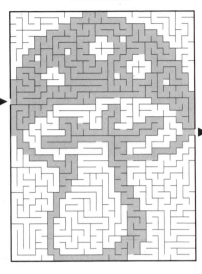

Maze #116

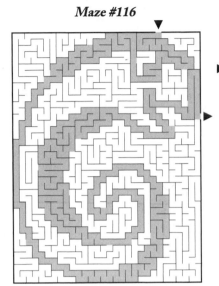

Maze #119

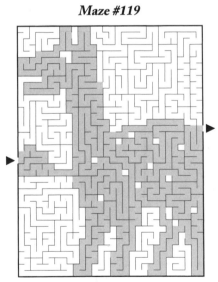

Maze #117

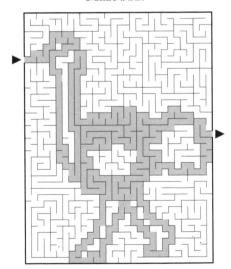

Solutions

Maze #120

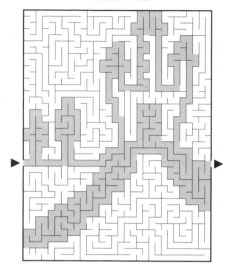

Maze #122

Maze #121

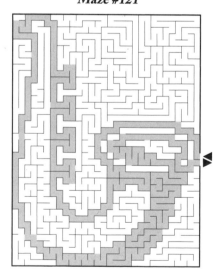

Maze #123

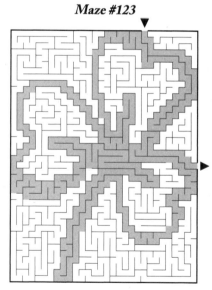

Solutions

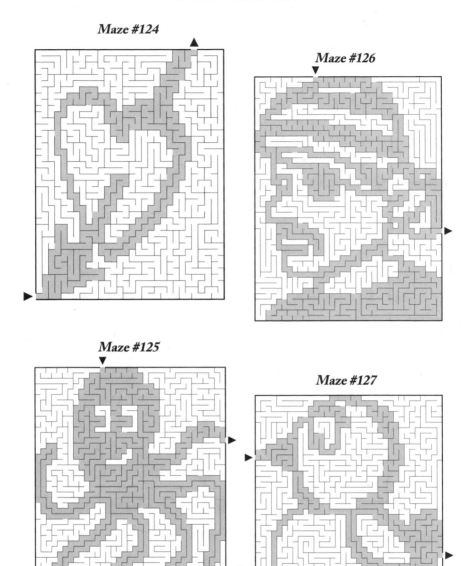

Maze #124

Maze #126

Maze #125

Maze #127

Solutions

Maze #128

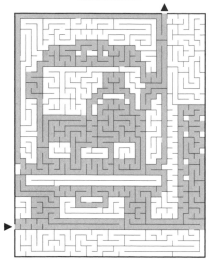

Maze #130

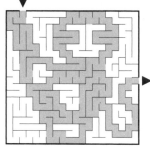

Maze #131

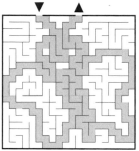

Maze #129

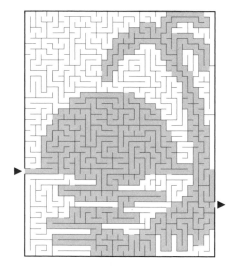

Maze #132

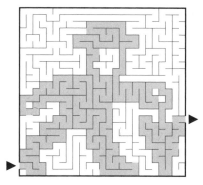

Solutions

Maze #136

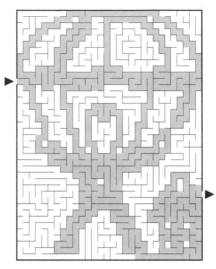

Maze #133

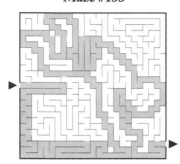

Maze #134

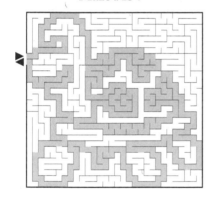

Maze #137

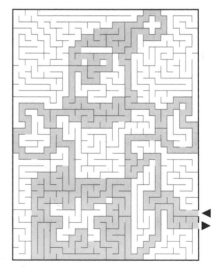

Maze #135

Solutions

Maze #138

Maze #140

Maze #139

Maze #141

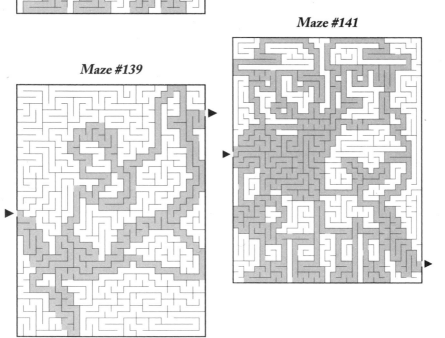

Solutions

Maze #142

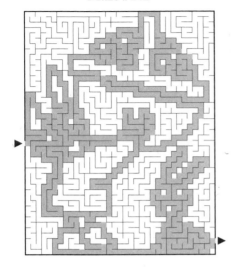

Maze #143

Maze #144

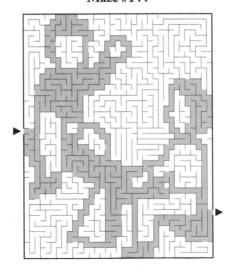

Solutions

Maze #146

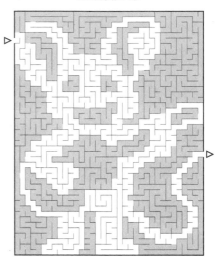

Maze #145

Maze #147

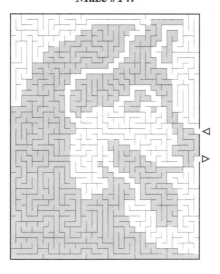

Solutions

Maze #148

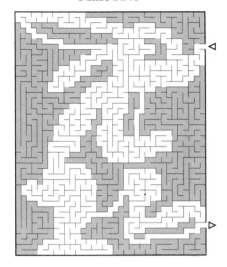

Maze #149

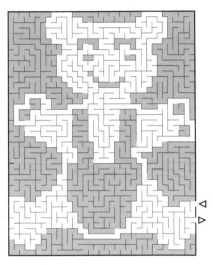

Maze #150

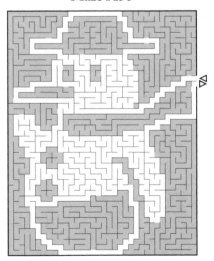

Solutions

Maze #152

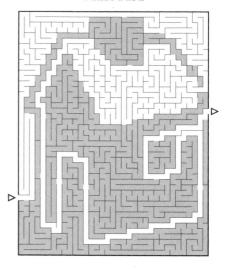

Maze #151

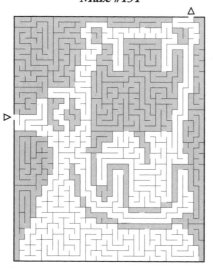

Maze #153

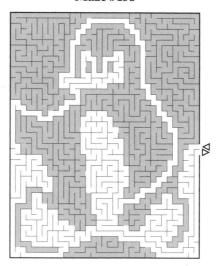

Solutions

Maze #154

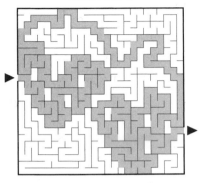

Maze #157

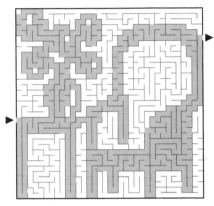

Maze #155

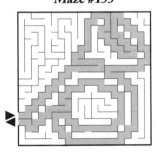

Maze #156

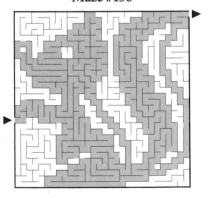

Maze #158

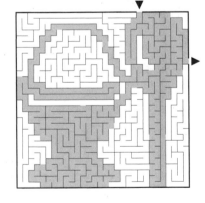

Maze #159

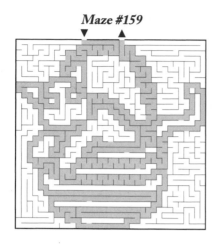

Maze #162

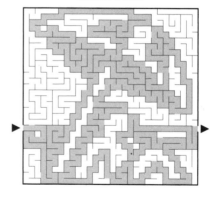

Maze #160

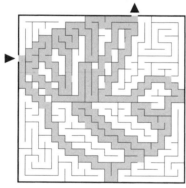

Maze #163

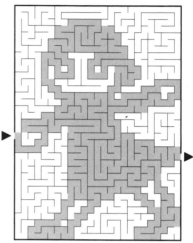

Maze #161

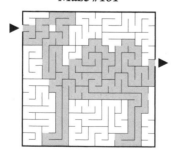

Solutions

Maze #166

Maze #164

Maze #165

Maze #167

Solutions

Maze #170

Maze #168

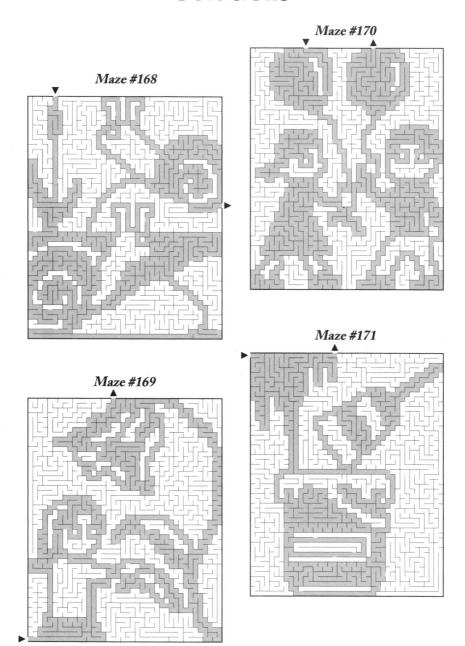

Maze #169

Maze #171

Solutions

Maze #172

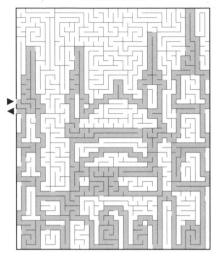

Maze #174

Maze #173

Maze #175

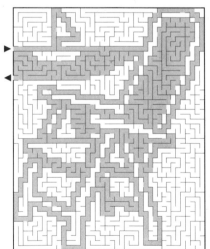

Solutions

Maze #176

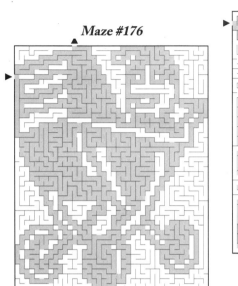

Maze #178

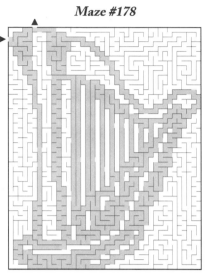

Maze #177

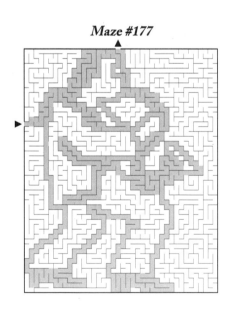

Maze #179

Solutions

Maze #180

Maze #182

Maze #181

Maze #183

Solutions

Maze #186

Maze #184

Maze #185

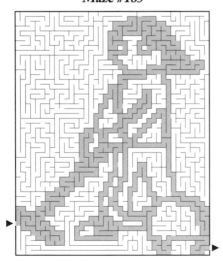

Maze #187

Solutions

Maze #188

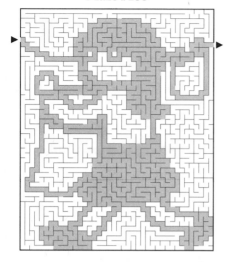

Maze #190

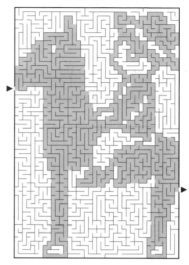

Maze #189

Maze #191

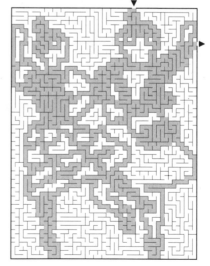

Solutions

Maze #194

Maze #192

Maze #195

Maze #193

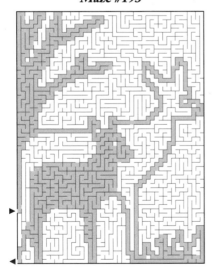

Solutions

Maze #196

Maze #198

Maze #197

Maze #199

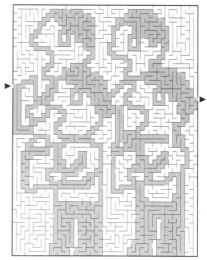

Solutions

Maze #202

Maze #200

Maze #203

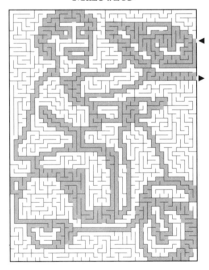

Maze #201

Solutions

Maze #204

Maze #206

Maze #205

Maze #207

Solutions

Maze #210

Maze #208

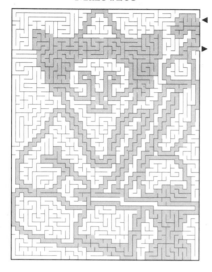

Maze #211

Maze #209

Solutions

Maze #212

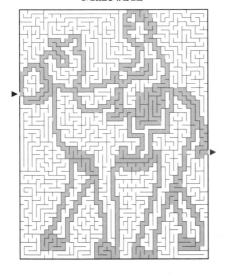

Maze #214

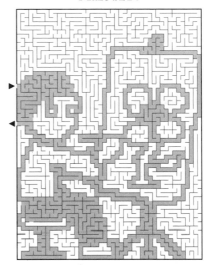

Maze #213

Maze #215

Solutions

Maze #218

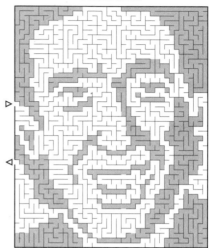

Tim Allen

Maze #216

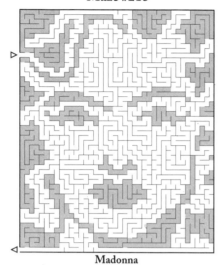

Madonna

Maze #219

Henry Winkler

Maze #217

Tori Spelling

Solutions

Maze #221

Maze #220

Maze #222

Solutions

Maze #223

Maze #224

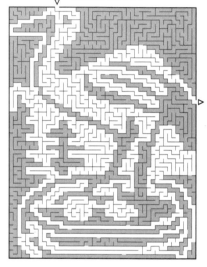

Maze #225

Solutions

Maze #227

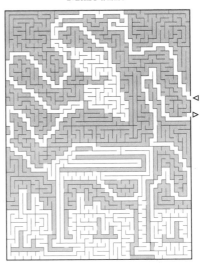

Maze #226

Maze #228

Solutions

Maze #231

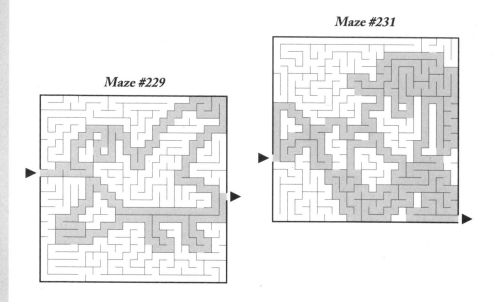

Maze #229

Maze #232

Maze #230

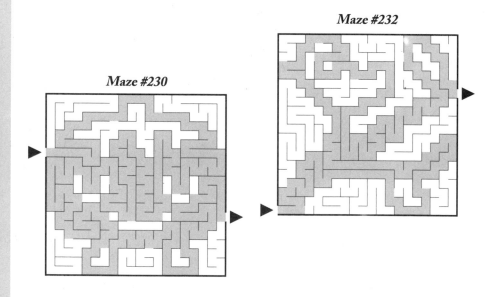

Solutions

Maze #233

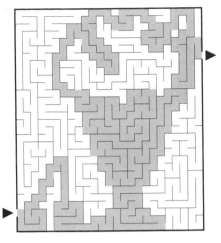

Maze #235

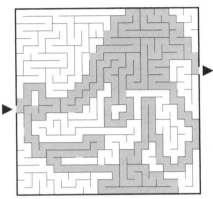

Maze #234

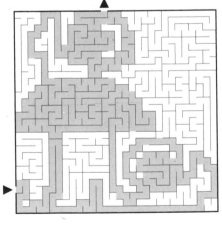

Maze #236

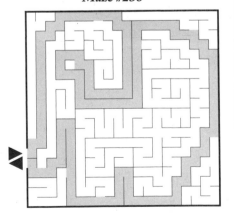

Solutions

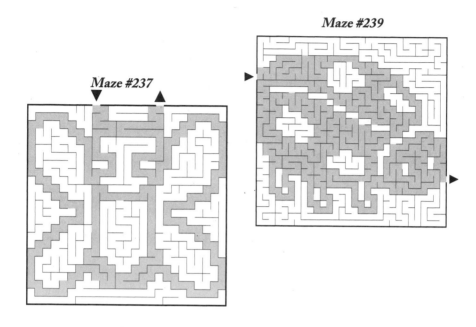

Maze #239

Maze #237

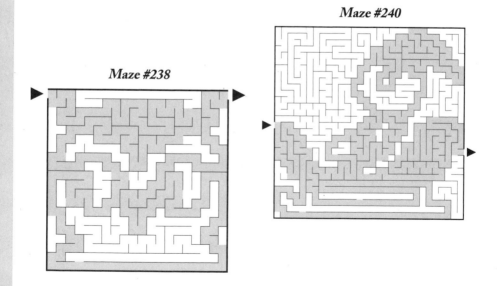

Maze #238

Maze #240

Solutions

Maze #241

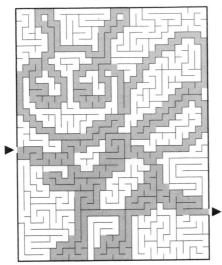

Maze #242

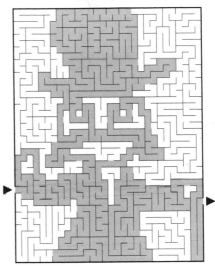

Maze #243

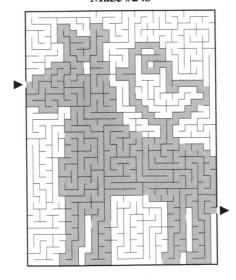

Solutions

Maze #245

Maze #244

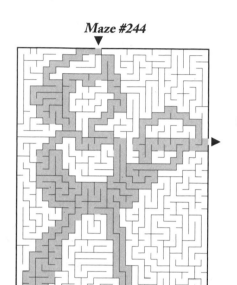

Maze #246

Solutions

Maze #247

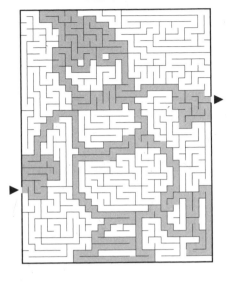

Maze #248

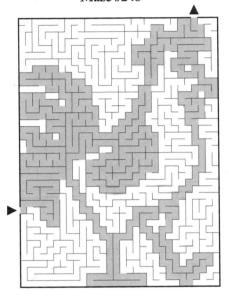

Maze #249

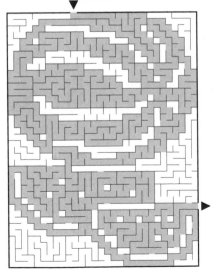

Solutions

Maze #251

Maze #250

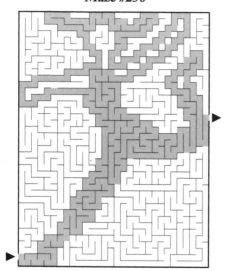

Maze #252

Solutions

Maze #253

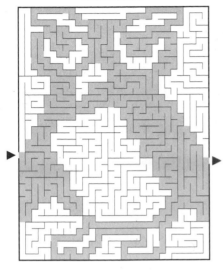

Maze #254

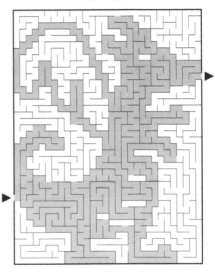

Maze #255

Solutions

Maze #257

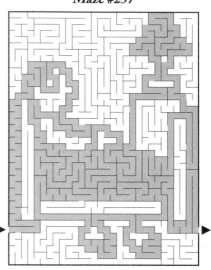

Maze #256

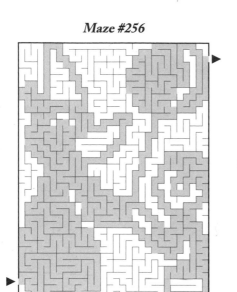

Maze #258

Solutions

Maze #259

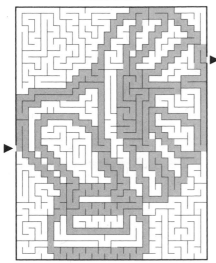

Maze #260

Maze #261

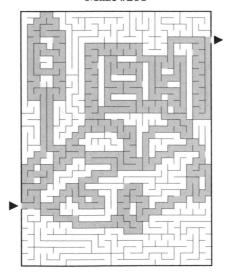

Solutions

Maze #263

Maze #262

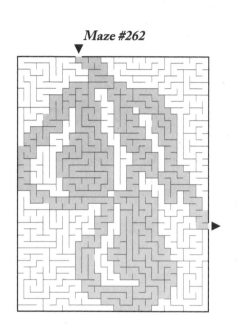

Maze #264

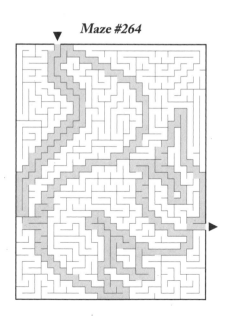

Solutions

Maze #265

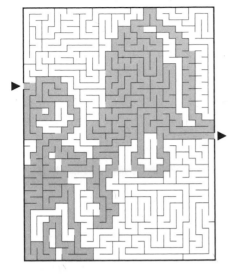

Maze #266

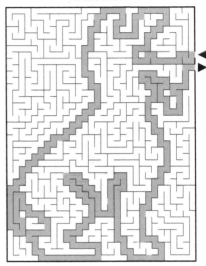

Maze #267

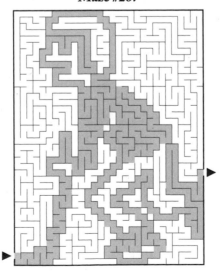

Solutions

Maze #269

Maze #268

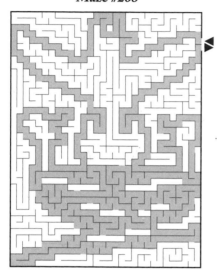

Maze #270

Solutions

Maze #271

Maze #272

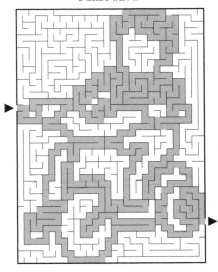

Maze #273

Solutions

Maze #275

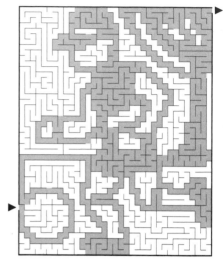

Maze #274

Maze #276

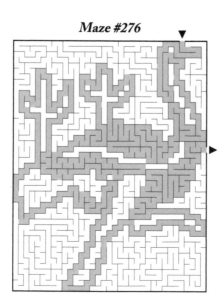

Solutions

Maze #277

Maze #278

Maze #279

Solutions

Maze #281

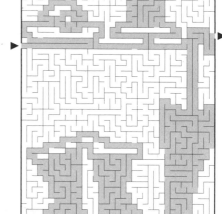

Maze #280

Maze #282

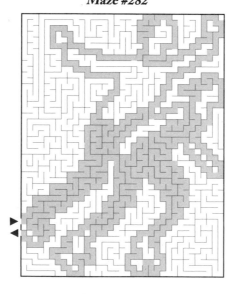

Solutions

Maze #283

Maze #284

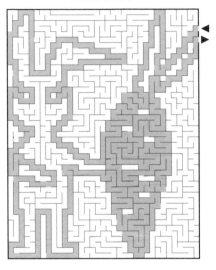

Maze #285

Solutions

Maze #287

Maze #286

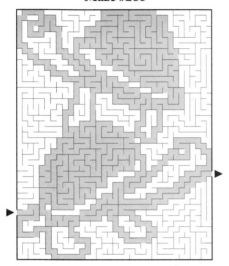

Maze #288

Solutions

Maze #289

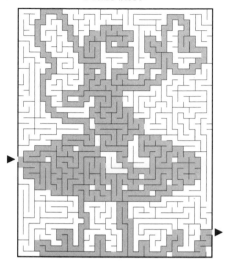

Maze #290

Maze #291

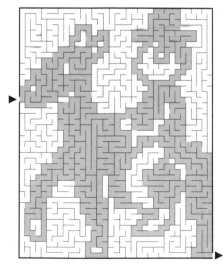

Solutions

Maze #293

Maze #292

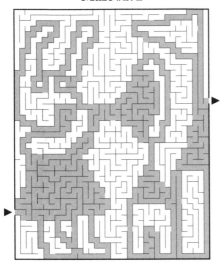

Maze #294

Solutions

Maze #295

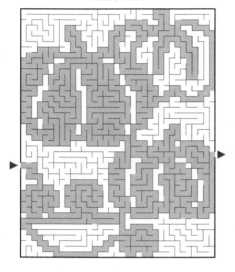

Maze #296

Maze #297

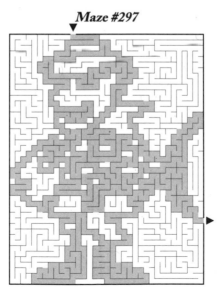

Solutions

Maze #299

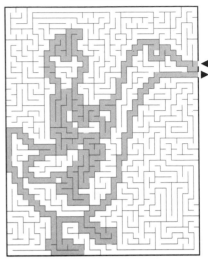

Maze #298

Maze #300

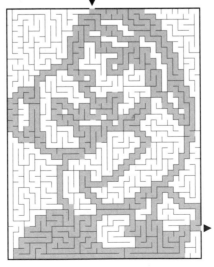

Solutions

Maze #301

Maze #302

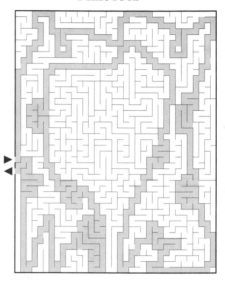

Maze #303

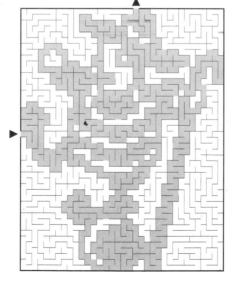

Solutions

Maze #304

Maze #305